D0386218

DEFROSTING ANTARCTIC SECRETS

by

Henry S. Francis, Jr. and Philip M. Smith

If you are interested in a career in the Antarctic, there are several government departments as well as private companies looking for qualified young people. So far it has been a man's world, but some day whole families may settle there. In order to become a young explorer in this exciting continent, there are several exacting qualifications: you must be trained in the physical sciences, navigation and repair of radios and automatic engines; know how to handle high explosives; know about mountaineering and rescue work and be self-reliant and durable. This is a rugged frontier of six million square miles, as big as the United States and half of Canada, the highest continent in the world, averaging seven to eight thousand feet above sea level, covered with ice and surrounded by ocean. The dangers and hardships are great, but the opening up of vast resources will yield great benefits to the world.

* * * * *

Classification and Dewey Decimal: Geography (919.9)

About the Authors:

HENRY S. FRANCIS and PHILIP M. SMITH work with the National Science Foundation's Antarctic Program. Born in Boston, Massachusetts and a graduate of Harvard, Henry Francis worked for the Arctic Institute of North America and later was Executive Assistant to the deputy chief scientist of the United States Program in Little America during the International Geophysical Year.

Philip Smith was born in Springfield, Ohio, and was educated at Ohio State University. He worked for the United States Army's Transportation Arctic Group and was one of a team of eleven which established the overland supply route between Little America and Byrd Station. A glaciologist by vocation, his interest also lies in the scientific exploration of caves. Both men live in the suburbs of Washington, D.C.

Defrosting Antarctic Secrets

Defrosting Antarctic Secrets

THE CHALLENGE OF THE FROZEN FRONTIER

by

Henry S. Francis, Jr.

and

Philip M. Smith

1967 FIRST CADMUS EDITION
THIS SPECIAL EDITION IS PUBLISHED BY ARRANGEMENT WITH THE PUBLISHERS OF THE REGULAR EDITION
COWARD-McCANN, INC.
BY
E. M. HALE AND COMPANY
EAU CLAIRE, WISCONSIN

Library of Congress Catalog Card Number: 62-10942

This edition lithographed in U.S.A. by Wetzel Brothers, Inc., Milwaukee, Wisconsin

DEDICATION

To Dr. Edward C. Thiel, who gave his life in pursuit of scientific exploration in Antarctica, November 8, 1961, at Wilkes Station.

ACKNOWLEDGMENTS

The authors wish to acknowledge the generous assistance of Mrs. Thelma Warner, without whom the manuscript would never have been prepared.

PICTURE SOURCES

Except where otherwise indicated, the pictures in this book are official U.S. Navy photos. For obtaining these, the publishers are particularly grateful to Commander R. L. Bufkins, Assistant Director of Media Relations in the Navy's Office of Information, and to Lieutenant J. W. Stierman, Assistant Head of the Magazine Book Branch.

Other pictures were supplied by the following sources:

Belgian Government Information Center, page 27
British Information Services, pages 20, 29, 30
Carleton College, page 42
Francis, Henry S., Jr., pages 57, 64, 67, 74, 75, 91, 95, 108
French Embassy Press and Information Division, page 25
Journal of Glaciology, March, 1961, pages 48, 53
New York Public Library, pages 24, 28, 32
Norwegian Travel Information Office, Nickolas Murray, page 31
University of Wisconsin, pages 50, 51
University of Wisconsin (Courtesy of Charles Bentley), page 46

Editor of this Series: Sabra Holbrook
Book Design: Gedeon Takaro

Contents

"And I tell you, if you have the desire for knowledge and the power to give it physical expression, go out and explore."
— *The Worst Journey in the World,* Apsley Cherry-Garrard.

The Antarctic and You

FOR EACH EXPLORER who goes to the Antarctic, there is a three-fold challenge. There is the challenge of opening up the world's last unexplored continent. There is the challenge of an environment to be overcome. There is the challenge of scientific discoveries which can benefit all mankind.

Studies of the earth's atmosphere above the South Pole may prove it to be a natural portal to outer space, and a vantage point from which to track satellites. Studies below Antarctic seas may help us find sources of food for the more than a billion and a half people in the world who go to bed hungry every night. Other discoveries may let us determine the effect of cold Antarctic air on the weather of the world.

As each explorer of the past has met Antarctic challenges, new opportunity has been created for those who followed him. Each new discovery has, in turn, posed new questions.

The first explorers realized something lay to the south beyond the floating ice. What was it? The next group found it was a continent. What lay inside it? More explorers penetrated its interior. What use could it be? The answer to that question is the goal of today's explorers. In their struggle to attain it, they are adding a new dimension to the Antarctic — international cooperation.

The early discovery of the continent was anything but cooperative. It was the result of competition between Great Britain, France, the Soviet Union (which was then called Russia) and the United States. Later, Argentina, Australia, Chile, Belgium, Japan, Norway, New Zealand and the Republic (then Union) of South Africa entered the contest. Each nation operated separately. Each tried to get ahead of the others. Men and nations began to feel possessive about Antarctica and to stake out claims.

Claims always mean fences. But fences and bound-

aries do not foster good scientific exploration, particularly in an area so huge that no one country has the means to explore it all.

So today nations have signed a treaty calling for a mutual effort to search out the secrets of the icy continent. As today's explorer meets its challenges, he works with men of 12 nations in pursuit of a common goal. That goal is to find the answers to the multitude of "whys," the new questions to which each discovery always leads. For instance:

How deep is the Antarctic ice?
How old is the snow?
How high is the continent?
What makes the "southern lights"?
How are icebergs born?

These are some of the questions for which you will find answers in this book. You will find many other questions for which there are no answers yet. Perhaps you will be among the young scientists who will come up with them. Antarctica is a continent for adventurous youth.

Even in the past, many members of the teams accompanying such famous explorers as Robert Falcon Scott were young men. Scott's assistant zoologist, Apsley Cherry-Garrard, was twenty-four years old. In some of the other early expeditions, the leaders themselves were in their twenties. Captain Nathaniel Palmer wasn't even twenty-one when he sighted the mountainous, island-bordered point which now bears his name, the Palmer or Antarctic Peninsula. His was the exciting discovery of the first great geographical feature of the continent, the extension that almost connects the Antarctic with South America.

A career in Antarctica is not only exciting, however, but also exacting. A young explorer must be well trained in physical sciences. He must also have skills in everyday matters: navigation, repair and operation of radio and of automotive engines. He must know how to handle explosives, and have had experience in mountaineering and crevasse rescue work. He needs knowledge of the history and geography of Antarctica.

The explorer must be self-reliant and durable. He must be in good physical condition to do his share of hard daily work. The work may be shoveling snow for drinking water or digging a ten-foot glaciological pit. It may be climbing a high pole in a shrieking snow-laden gale to repair a radio antenna, or just the seemingly endless task of moving heavy boxes in a storeroom.

The man of the Antarctic must be friendly. He must be capable of getting along with others for weeks and months in a crowded vehicle or small station. Some or all of his fellow workers may speak a different language and have entirely different views and customs. Finally,

Probing a crevasse

he must have the will power to keep going when everything seems useless.

It has been a man's world in Antarctica so far. In the future, however, women will also have an opportunity to meet the challenge of Antarctic living. They will go as nurses and scientists, surveyors, and maintenance workers for engines and radios.

One day entire families may go to Antarctica. They will have to learn the lesson of all pioneers: how to raise and educate their children and teach them to be at home in the wilderness.

Several departments of the U. S. Government as well as private educational institutions are looking for young people eager to make careers of Antarctic discovery. The government agency that serves as a kind of central clearing point for all such opportunities is the National Science Foundation.

If you are one of those who respond to this opportunity yours will be a satisfaction of personal endeavor as great — perhaps greater — than that of the first men who saw the frozen continent.

Today's men of the Antarctic

The U.S.S. Glacier and the track she made through frozen seas off East Antarctica, February, 1960

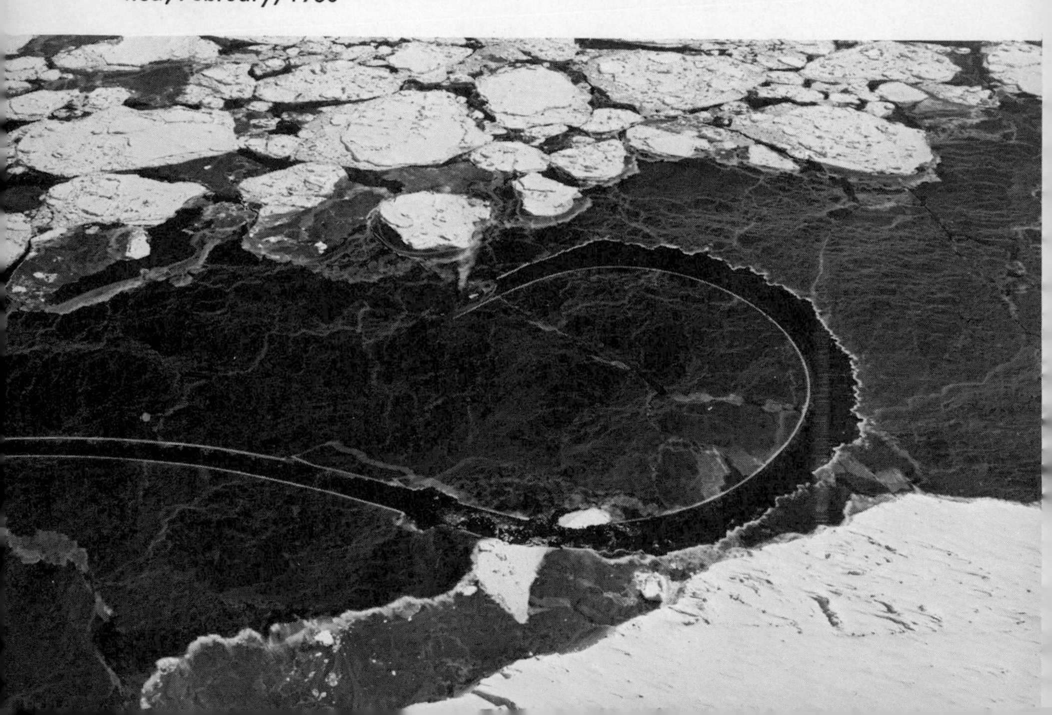

1. Young Discoverers

ENSIGN BEN KOETHER took the sextant from his eye and strode to his chart table on the bridge of the ship. Laying his navigation instrument aside, he replotted the ship's position and looked out once more across the cold blue and white expanse of water, sea ice and icebergs. South, ahead of the ship, he saw a mountain. Yes, this was it. This was land in an unexplored part of the Antarctic, along the eastern edge of the continent.

Ben reported to the captain of the ship. They would follow the coast east, the captain said, mapping as they went. Ben was a little nervous about taking the ship into uncharted waters. He had reason to be. He was only twenty-three and the navigator of the U. S. Navy's large icebreaker, the U.S.S. *Glacier*. The ship was where no ship had been before. It was mid-February 1960.

More mountains came into sight. A few were craggy peaks of gray rock, bare above the ice. Ben Koether plotted them on his chart as they appeared. Slowly a new coastline began to emerge.

Men had been trying to reach this coast for a long time. More than 100 years ago, in 1839, Lt. William Walker, another young naval officer like Ben Koether, had tried. Walker was the captain of the *Flying Fish*. This 27-ton wooden vessel was part of the United States' first official venture in Antarctic exploration. The *Flying Fish* wasn't well equipped for work in the Antarctic Ocean. The heavy ice pack nearly crushed the little ship 120 miles off the coast.

Between the voyages of Walker and Koether, men came no closer to this coast. They reached other portions of the continent and left this ice-packed sea for present-day explorers. Only now are we beginning to explore these last unknown portions of the last unknown continent.

Today men approach the coast of the Antarctic with powerful steel-hulled icebreakers. Even so, disaster may strike them suddenly. As you read these words, one of them may be held fast in the grip of grinding ice. A party of men and tractors may be caught among great, hidden, treacherous fissures in the ice cap.

Before the Antarctic explorers lies a frontier of six million square miles, an area as big as the United States and half of Canada. It is the highest continent* in the world, averaging between 7,000 and 8,000 feet above sea level. The great ice dome covering much of it rises to 13,000 feet. Elsewhere mountains stick up through the ice to 16,000 feet or higher. No one yet knows which mountain is the highest.

Antarctica is remote and surrounded by a great ocean which separates it from all other land. The ocean holds another barrier, the floating ice pack.

Even before this pack is reached, other dangers beset a would-be explorer. Between 23½ degrees and 66 degrees south, a 2,500-mile-wide band of water stretches around the earth. Here warm winds move from west to

---

* Or continent*s*. It may be two of them.

east without interruption. There are no large bodies of land to stop them. This warm air is also fed from the south by cold air blowing off the Antarctic polar ice cap. The cold air mixes with the warm air to make great circular — and often violent — air movements, or cyclones.

In the high latitudes of this region, ocean currents from the Temperate Zone of the south meet cold currents from the Antarctic. The line at which this Temperate Zone ends and the Antarctic begins is called the Antarctic Convergence. There the cold currents dive below the warmer temperate currents, then travel slowly northward on the ocean bottom. Because of the rapid change of temperature that takes place in a matter of a few miles in this area, the weather is often cloudy and foggy. The combination of the very cold and warm air and water and merciless wind makes this 2,500-mile belt the world's worst sailing region.

to South America

to Africa

Deception Island

Palmer Peninsula

Weddell Sea

Filchner Ice Shelf

Bellinghausen Sea

Pensacola Mountains

Sentinel Mountains

WEST ANTARCTICA

South Pole

EAST ANTARCTICA

to Asia

Horlick Mountains

Bentley's canyon

Marie Byrd Land

Knox Coast (Wilkes Coast)

Amundsen Sea

Byrd Station

Queen Maud Mountains

Ross Ice Shelf

Little America

Wilkes Station

Kainan Bay

Cape Crozier

Cape Evans

McMurdo Sound

Ross Sea

McMurdo Air Station

Adelie Coast

to New Zealand

to Australia

South of the Convergence, the surface of the polar ocean freezes every winter. The ice may be anywhere from a few inches to 12 feet thick. Each summer warmer weather melts part of it, but a great ice belt almost always remains around the Antarctic. The belt tends to hold down the ocean waves so that the sea beneath is calm. Yet the ice itself is subject to the currents, the tides and the winds. As these forces change, pressures develop in the ice. Cracks or leads are formed. Ice blocks are pushed up onto each other in ridges known as pressure ridges. The sea ice is constantly moving and working.

Projecting from the Antarctic coast itself are numerous ice shelves and tongues of glaciers. An ice shelf is a great floating platform, built up from ice flowing down from the ice cap that covers the continent. The shelf is covered and increased by an accumulation of snow every year. The ice stretches and pushes out into the open sea. About one seventh of this mass floats above the ocean surface.

Ice shelves are about 800 to 900 feet thick on their outer or sea edge. As this edge is weakened by stretching, pieces break off and float to sea, and travel with the winds and currents. A hunk of ice may be a few cubic feet in size or as big as the state of Connecticut. Sighted at sea, these broken hunks of shelf are called icebergs.

A ship working in the ice near the coast must look out for bergs as well as the pack. It has to avoid triple perils. It must stay off uncharted rocks, away from the icebergs and out of the clutches of the pack ice.

You can see why it has taken men two hundred years

just to approach the land. The first man actually to cross the Antarctic Circle was a British captain, James Cook. In 1772, with two small ships, he sailed around the Antarctic. But he never saw the coast of the continent. His little vessels couldn't sail far into the shield of floating ice that surrounds it.

Iceberg

Pack ice

Captain Cook

A great southern continent, however, was suspected before the voyage of Captain Cook. The search for a trade route to the East Indies and Asia had forced ships around the Cape of Good Hope at Africa's tip and Cape Horn at the bottom of South America. Blown off course in high seas around these capes, the ships' crews discovered southerly islands as early as 1675. South of these islands sailors found nothing but a cold ocean and ice.

However, the spices and silks of the Orient weren't the only prizes for sailing ships. Whale oil and the fur of the seal brought good prices also. In Cook's wake, more adventurous captains risked their ships and crews in the southern oceans near the edge of the ice. They formed trading companies to hunt the great blue whale, the sperm whale and the fur seal. In pursuit of oil and fur, daring captains began to make unexpected geographical discoveries.

Ships in harbor of Deception Island

Nathaniel Palmer was one of these captains. He commanded the 45-ton sloop *Hero*, one of five ships of a fleet from Stonington, Connecticut. The *Hero* was no bigger than a modern motor yacht. Palmer had discovered an island with a protected southern harbor in a sunken volcanic crater. The narrow entrance to the harbor was difficult to see from the ocean. For this reason Palmer called the island Deception Island. From this haven, he set out in the *Hero* to confirm reports of islands to the south and to find more seals. It was the year 1820. Captain Palmer was less than twenty-one years old.

Sailing through the Antarctic Convergence, Palmer learned why its latitudes were called the Roaring Forties (40–50 degrees south), the Furious Fifties (50–60 degrees south), and the Screaming Sixties (60 degrees). The names describe the climate well.

As Captain Palmer sailed on, he would often find himself in a fog, amid great pieces of sea ice or icebergs that had floated into the warmer water from the frozen seas to the south. These pieces of ice, largely submerged below the ocean surface, were much heavier and bigger than his little ship. To run onto one of them in the fog would mean destruction. To go too far into the broken ice would be to risk being trapped and crushed if the wind should change and blow the ice together.

Like Captain Cook before him, Palmer had to be content to remain on the outer edge of the ice pack, but he discovered the southern islands he was seeking as well as the peninsula named for him.

By 1840 exploration and discovery had become as big an interest as whale oil and fur seals. Many private explorers and four national expeditions had set out. All four sought the frozen continent itself, not merely its outlying islands and points. The first of these expeditions was led by Thaddeus von Bellingshausen, a German captain who sailed for the Czar of Russia in 1820. He didn't reach or even sight the continent, but his name was given to the great icebound sea that lies southeast of the Antarctic Peninsula, the Bellingshausen Sea whose coastline Koether was to map 140 years later.

Base at Palmer Peninsula today

James Ross

Around 1840 the leaders of the other three national expeditions also gave their names to parts of the Antarctic. In 1841, James Ross led a British expedition into the Ross Sea. He sailed his ships farther south than any of the other three.

Dumont d'Urville

Dumont d'Urville led a French expedition in 1840 which landed on the Adélie Coast, south of the Australian island of Tasmania. He arrived only a few weeks after Lieutenant Charles Wilkes of the U. S. Navy had sighted the continent in that region.

Lieutenant Wilkes sailed east, 1,700 miles. He skirted the coast, mapping its features as he went. Wilkes dared the dangers of the polar sea inside the ice.

Approaching the pack ice, he sought out a lead or crack and followed it until another lead was found or until it became necessary to retrace his route and try again. He risked the possibility that the lead would close about his ship and trap it. Locked in the ice, the sides of the ship could be slowly crushed by pressure. Only quick release would be able to save it.

Huge icebergs and uncharted rocks were also dangers for Wilkes and his men. Time and time again they nearly met disaster. Finally, as the summer advanced and the days grew shorter and the temperatures colder, Wilkes had to abandon his voyage along the coast. He had seen more of it than any explorer up to that time.

Wilkes Land was named for him. From the Adélie Coast to the Knox Coast, he drew rough maps of ice-free areas, of floating tongues of glaciers, hills and mountains, coves and bays.

For nearly fifty years no expeditions reached farther into Antarctica than Wilkes had, but by 1900 another generation of young men were again in search of new frontiers. They followed the routes of Wilkes, Ross and d'Urville. This group included some men who were to become very famous explorers: Adrien de Gerlache, Robert Falcon Scott, Ernest Shackleton, Roald Amundsen and Douglas Mawson. These men came to explore inside the continent as well as new sections of its coast.

Adrien de Gerlache, a young Belgian explorer, was the first to spend a winter in Antarctica. His stay wasn't intentional.

Adrien de Gerlache

To the southwest of the Palmer Peninsula, de Gerlache sailed into a very treacherous pack. His ship, the *Belgica*, became stuck between the ice floes. For six months in 1898, the *Belgica* drifted helplessly at the mercy of the winds and ocean currents. De Gerlache and his men learned to eat seal and penguin and how to protect themselves in low temperatures and high winds. They worked outside around the immobile ship during the winter darkness, studying marine life and the action of sea ice. When their ship was finally released from the ice, they returned home bringing with them the first scientific data from the continent, and much valuable knowledge about its climate and how to survive in it.

C. E. Borchgrevink

A year later a scientific party from a British expedition lead by C. E. Borchgrevink spent the first winter on the Antarctic continent itself at Cape Adare.

Using the experience of the de Gerlache and Borchgrevink parties in how to survive the Antarctic winter,

Captain Robert Falcon Scott

an Englishman, Robert Falcon Scott, planned a great wintering expedition in 1902. Leaving his ship, the *Discovery*, in McMurdo Sound, part of the Ross Sea, he and two companions set off toward the South Pole by sled. They crossed the floating Ross Ice Shelf and discovered the mountains on its southern boundary.

Scott's expedition, more than any previous one, inspired young men to seek polar work as a profession. One of those inspired was Ernest Shackleton, who had sledged on the ice shelf with Scott. He returned to Antarctica with his own team in 1907.

Shackleton took ponies to pull his sleds, but only a few of them proved surefooted enough not to flounder in the snow and hardy enough to stand the strain of it. So Shackleton and three companions marched. They used the few steady ponies to pull their supplies.

Sir Ernest Shackleton

They went beyond Scott's farthest point, discovering a route through the great mountains south of the Ross Ice Shelf. The route led up a glacier.

Ice in a glacier is in motion. As it creeps over rocky obstructions and cliffs the ice splits apart, forming crevasses often more than 100 feet deep. Constant wind fills them with snow. The entrances become concealed.

On the glacier the last of Shackleton's ponies slipped and fell into a deep crevasse. There was no way to save him. The men walked on, hauling their own supplies, to a point 97 miles from the Pole. Then food ran low. Shackleton turned back. He provided explorers with a great rule: Never go too far. In three expeditions to Antarctica Shackleton never lost a man in parties under his personal command.

Still the Pole evaded those who sought it. Scott

Captain Roald Amundsen

wanted to reach it. The Norwegian Amundsen did, too. Both set out with expeditions in 1911. Scott took scientists who worked in a number of different parties, all probing out from a base at McMurdo Sound. Amundsen concentrated on the race to the Pole.

Apsley Cherry-Garrard (third from left, seated) at a birthday dinner with Scott, end of table

Apsley Cherry-Garrard was twenty-four years old when he was selected as a member of Scott's second Antarctic expedition. Cherry-Garrard's qualifications were a college degree, some knowledge of zoology, and plenty of strength and enthusiasm.

His handicap was bad nearsightedness requiring him to wear thick glasses. On the trail his glasses frosted up, making him stumble. Yet if he didn't wear them he could barely see the way ahead. He had accidents, but he survived them.

At Scott's camp at Cape Evans on Ross Island, Cherry-Garrard learned his first lessons about the Antarctic. He learned to work long hours in summer, taking advantage of the season's constant sunshine. While working hard, he learned to pace himself so as not to expend his energy too quickly. He learned how to live and work inside, in cramped huts; to tent outside in the bitter cold. He learned the difficulty of pulling sleds through deep, soft snow on the surface of the ice shelf. But he also learned the excitement of sledging into the unknown. By the time the first winter had come, Cherry-Garrard was an experienced, capable expedition member.

Scott's camp at Cape Evans, exterior

Interior of camp when reopened 47 years after Scott's death

Restoration of camp interior, done by New Zealand government

Mummified by ice, husky found at camp

Letters received by Cherry-Garrard, found in Scott's hut

During the long winter, while Scott prepared for his push to the Pole, others studied Antarctic nature. Zoologist Cherry-Garrard was interested in Emperor penguins. In order to see one of their rookeries, he and two others made a perilous trip from their Cape Evans base to Cape Crozier during the dark winter. Only a distance of 30 air miles, the route took them across the ice shelf, over crevasses, up steep cliffs, and around boulders the size of trucks. The temperature dropped as low as −75 degrees Fahrenheit. The storms were frightful and darkness made the trip two or three times as hard as it would have been in daylight. But the team brought back the first egg of the Emperor penguin ever collected. Cherry-Garrard discovered that these birds start raising their young in the dead of winter. This astounded scientists. How could they hatch eggs and bring up the chicks at such low temperatures!

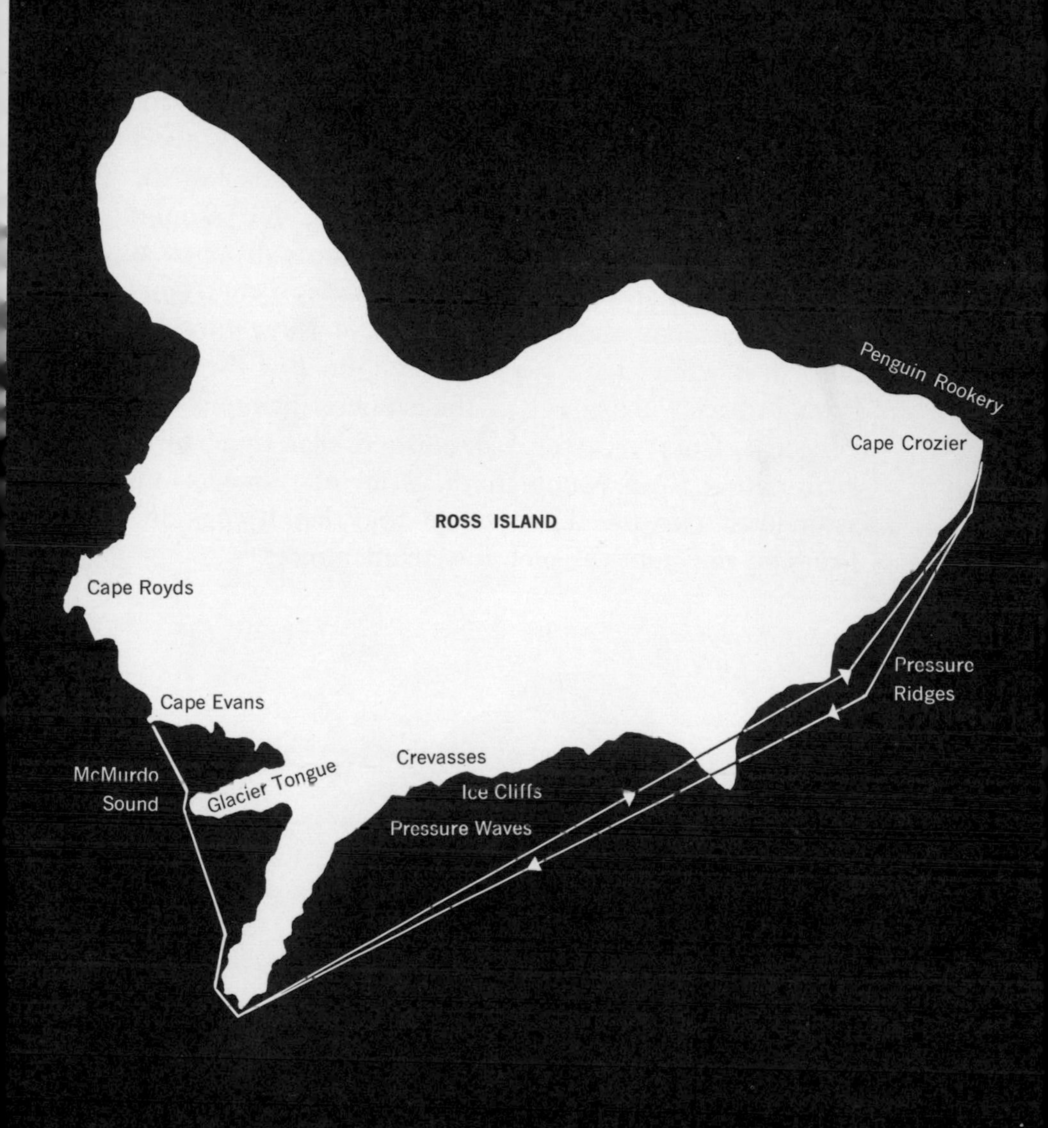

Cherry-Garrard's winter journey

The penguins' secret is that they keep the eggs on their flippers, partly surrounded by a flap of skin and fatty tissue. When one parent wants to go off to feed, the other one takes the egg. When the penguin chicks are hatched, they, too, huddle on their parents' flippers.

Not long after Cherry-Garrard's winter trip to Cape Crozier, Scott and his party set out for the Pole. After accompanying the group for part of the way and laying caches of food for them, Cherry-Garrard and a number of others returned to camp. They spent a long winter wondering what had become of Scott and the four companions who had gone with him. In the spring they sledged out in search of the expedition. They found Scott's last camp. He and his party had perished. Amundsen had beaten them to the Pole.

Ten years after his return to England, Cherry-Garrard wrote an account of his experiences which inspired many more people to polar work. Such adventurous accounts appealed especially to youth. When Richard Byrd began his long Antarctic career in 1929, he had no trouble finding eager young men to accompany him. In the next 18 years Byrd penetrated beyond the Pole and succeeded in photomapping a great part of the coastline as well as founding Little America and discovering Marie Byrd Land in West Antarctica.

Many young men who went with Byrd never left polar exploration thereafter. Among them was Laurence M. Gould. Fresh from college when he started, Larry Gould, a geologist, was bent on finding out more about the geology of the Antarctic interior.

In 1929–30, Larry and four companions set out by dog team for the great cliffs at the southern edge of the

Admiral Byrd

Ross Ice Shelf. The mountains were part of the chain discovered by Scott, Shackleton and Amundsen. Gould believed the rock in these mountains would tell him something of the history of the continent.

This 1,500-mile trip took him to places where fossils — traces of old plant and animal specimens — helped him date the age of the rocks and determine different stages of Antarctic climate. He discovered that some areas had once been warmer. (More recently, fossils have been found proving that there were once ferns and trees and running water on the continent.) By contrast, in other places near glaciers tumbling through the mountains, the rocks revealed that even more ice than at present had once covered the Antarctic. Gravel

Antarctic glacier

and stones, perched high on cliffs, were evidence that glaciers bigger than the current ones had once scoured these cliffs with their grinding, sliding, crushing motion. Larry also suspected that Antarctica might be two continents, not one, with an ice-choked trench between them.

This long trip provided the first large amount of scientific knowledge about the interior of Antarctica. On the basis of it, scientists began to speculate about how the continent had formed, and whether it *was* one or two. They began guessing about the depth of the great ice plateau. Larry's trip was the beginning of a series of long treks that would probe into the temperature and thickness of the ice and the nature of the rocks it clasped.

These treks are still going on today. From some of

Larry Gould

them we know that the base rock in East Antarctica is probably 400 to 500 million years old. On top of it are a series of sediments ranging in age from as little as 70 million years to as much as 250 million. The ice age — in millions of years — seems to be comparatively recent, and less "icy" than it once was.

In the 120 years, from the time young Nathaniel Palmer sailed south for seals to the year that Larry Gould sledged in search of rocks, explorers had moved from the rim of Antarctica to its Pole. They had probed its shield of ice and learned to travel over its face, but they still knew comparatively little about what lay above and below it. They couldn't yet answer questions the rest of the world was beginning to ask. How did this empty continent get that way? Of what use could it be to people?

2. 1,200 Miles Across the Ice Cap and 14,000 Feet Below

THE FACE OF ANTARCTICA is never at rest. The surface is ever changing. Wind is constantly blowing the snow that covers the ice. The blowing snow erodes other snow. It piles up *sastrugi*, weird mounds and hummocks.

But if the face of the continent is restless, so is the explorer. The work of scientists like Larry Gould raised questions about the structure of the continent, the thickness of the ice and snow. Exactly when did the ice age begin? Is it one very long period, or have there been several periods, as in North America? How did these ice shelves form? What does the land under the ice look like now?

To answer these and other questions the biggest of all expeditions to Antarctica was organized. It was part of a study of the entire earth coordinated by the International Council of Scientific Unions, and known as the IGY, the International Geophysical Year. The Antarctic portion of the study was scheduled to last from January 1957 through December 1958. Actually, the Antarctic studies have gone on ever since.

Twenty-seven-year-old Charlie Bentley of Buffalo, New York, was one of those who applied to be a member of the great IGY expedition to Antarctica. A Ph.D. in geology from Columbia University in New York City, Charlie had already spent several months measuring the thickness of the ice cap on Greenland. He wanted to measure the depth of the Antarctic cap. He believed that if he could trace the relationships of the mountain ranges beneath it, he could develop Gould's idea of an Antarctic trench. He could help map the land below the ice.

Charlie's assistant, Ned Ostenso, was a thirty-one-year-old student at the University of Wisconsin. The other members of Charlie's team were Bill and Jack Long and Vernon Anderson.

The Long brothers had already learned to love the wilderness. Bill, twenty-six, had climbed and skied in the Sierra Nevada mountains of his native California, and been a member of a climbing team in the Himalayas in Asia. His major at the University of Nevada had been geology.

Left to right: (rear) Jack Long, Vernon Anderson, Bill Long and friend; (front) Charlie Bentley and Ned Ostenso

From winter experience with the U. S. Forest Service, making avalanche surveys in the Sierras, Jack Long knew how to drive and repair vehicles equipped for snow travel. He obtained a position as a traverse engineer on Charlie's team. The job required repairing vehicles en route — traverse being Antarctic jargon for caravan.

Thirty-four-year-old Vernon Anderson, a graduate of the University of Chicago, planned to make snow studies.

After several weeks on the coast, the team spent its first winter 646 miles inland at Byrd Station. In succeeding summers, their traverses would take them many miles across Marie Byrd Land. They used their first winter to study all available information on that part of the continent which is in West Antarctica.

There wasn't much information. Admiral Byrd had sighted part of this great plateau from a plane. On a second trip, he had spotted mountains which he named the Horlicks. They seemed to separate the plateau from the Pole.

Later, Lincoln Ellsworth had flown from Palmer Peninsula, over the northern part of the plateau of West Antarctica, and landed in Little America. He reported that the plateau was as high as Denver, Colorado, in most places. Yet it was almost featureless. Ellsworth sighted one inland mountain range which he named the Sentinels.

As Charlie Bentley studied these past explorations, he worked out the details of a bold plan of action. On 1,200-mile-long trips in two successive summers, he planned to study the region north of Byrd Station to the

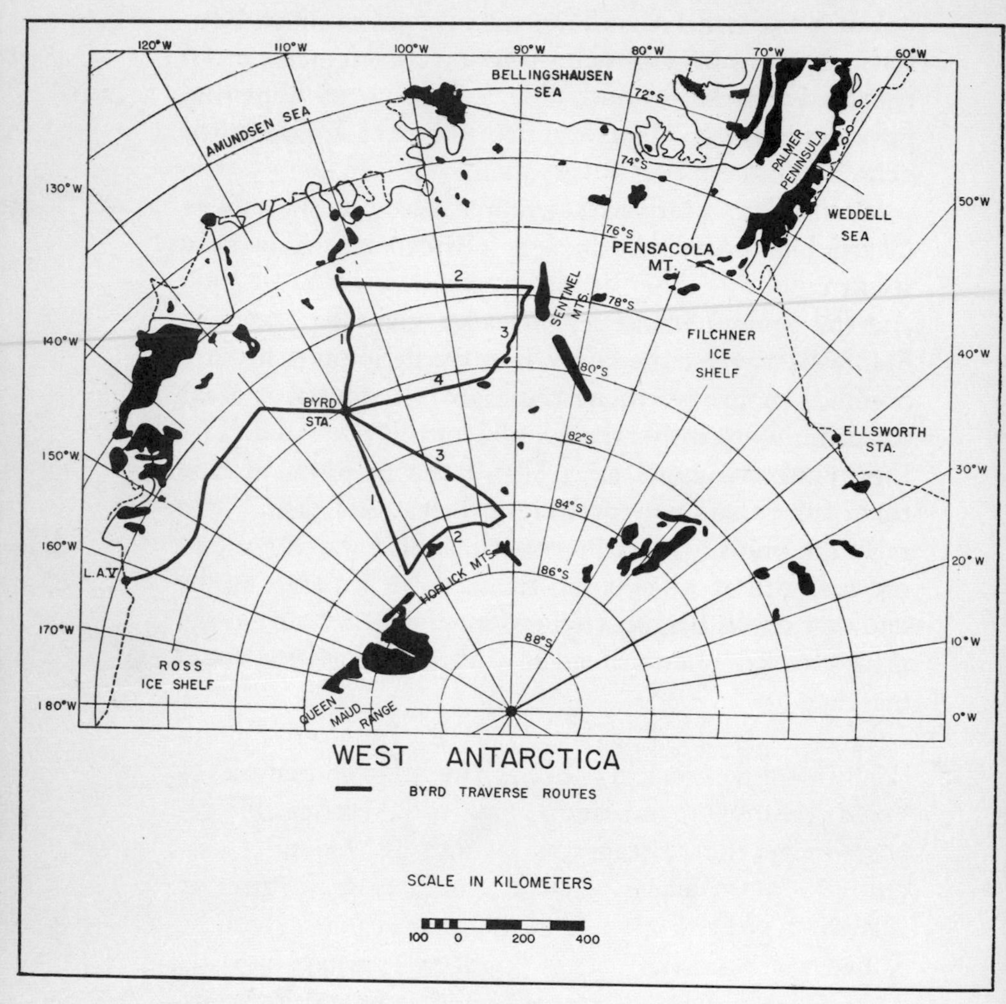

The Bentley traverses

Sentinel Mountains and south of the station to the Horlick Mountains.

For these trips Charlie planned to use three Sno-Cats. These are gasoline-powered vehicles with metal tracks. There are four tracks, each on a pontoon that provides enough "floatation" to keep the 7,000-pound vehicle from sinking into soft snow. The Sno-Cat is powerful. It can pull a tremendous load. Behind each of Charlie's three vehicles was a sled capable of holding six or eight 50-gallon drums of gasoline, crates of food and the equipment needed to make scientific studies.

On the traverse the Sno-Cats were this young group's home. The men slept and ate and did much of their scientific work inside the cats. Inside also was the radio they used to contact their base and a compass to help them steer their way across the featureless cap. Naturally the Sno-Cats were crowded. When it was time to eat, scientific work and papers had to be put aside so the cooking could begin. Then when it was time to sleep, things had to be moved again so the sleeping bags could

Sno-Cat

be brought out. Each morning everything was rearranged and made ready for work or travel.

On the traverse Charlie Bentley and Ned Ostenso spent most of their time determining the ice thickness and the nature of the rock below it. To do so they used a seismograph.

The seismograph records sound made by setting off explosives. Geophones, which are highly sensitive listeners, pick up the sound or echo and transmit it to the

Ned Ostenso sets geophones

The blast

seismograph instrument. The instrument then traces the echoes on photographic paper.

On the traverse 24 geophones were generally placed in the snow. When the team stopped to make camp, Ned Ostenso put on skis, packed the geophones and a long reel of wire on a small sled, and started out to plant them. He spaced them evenly, usually over a mile.

While Ned set out the geophones, Charlie set the amplification controls on the seismograph instrument panel and checked the machine's photographic recorder to make sure it was working properly. Then he gave a sign for everyone on the traverse to be still so nothing would confuse the sound. When he signaled Ned, Ned set off a small charge of explosive, which he had buried at a depth of about 15 feet. The distance from the spot where the explosive was set off down to the rock bottom below the ice was determined by the length of time the seismograph showed that it took for the sound of the explosive to echo back from the bottom. As long as Charlie knew how long it took sound to travel through an icy coating, he could figure out the ice thickness.

Differences between the times of the echo at either end of the line also told him whether and in what direction the rock sloped beneath the ice. By making shots ten or so miles from the geophones, he could tell how fast the sound traveled in the rock, and this helped him find out what kind of rock it was.

A seismic station was made every thirty miles all the way around the 1,200-mile loop from Byrd Station to the distant mountains and back. These records enabled Charlie to draw a map of the land beneath the ice cap. Here it is:

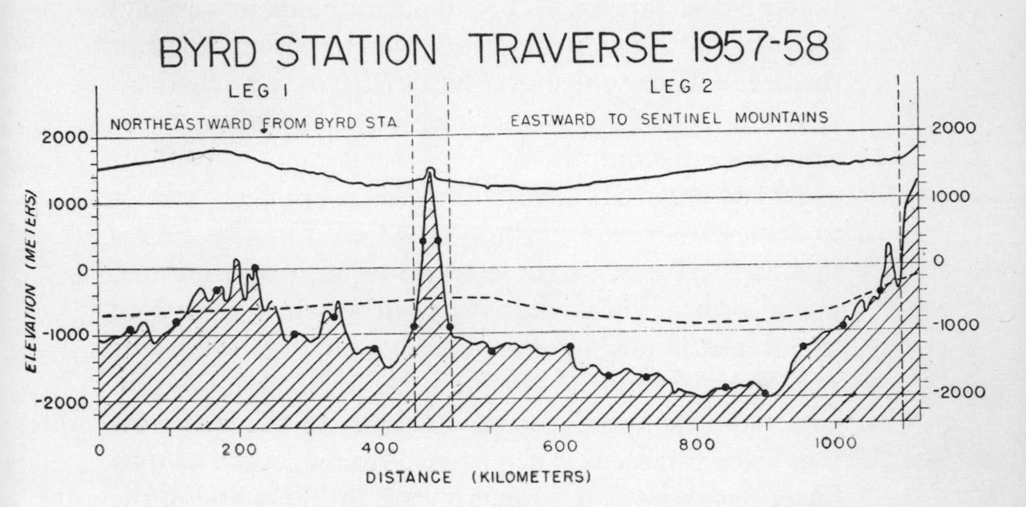

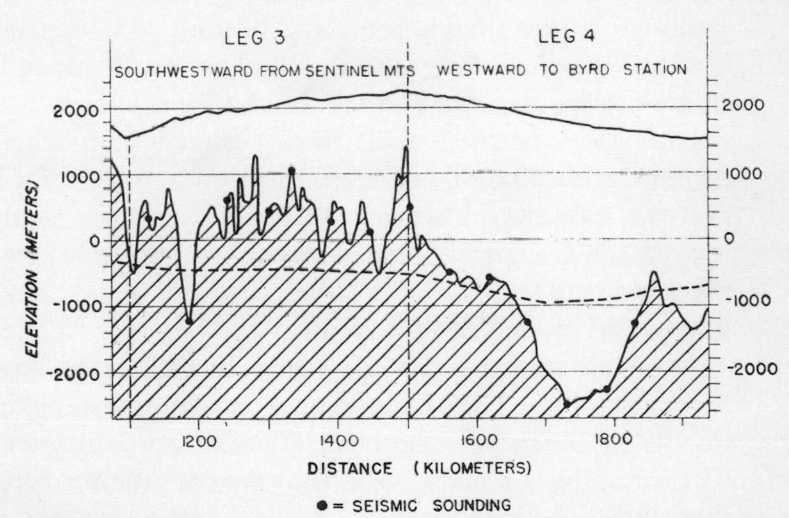

Profile along the Sentinel Mountains traverse route. Dashed line represents adjusted sea-level

To supplement the records obtained with the seismic equipment, Ned Ostenso also made gravity measurements.

The earth's pull, its gravity, is not the same everywhere on its surface. It is a tiny bit greater at the Poles because the earth is flattened there and its radius is smaller. The amount of pull is also affected by the kind of rocks that make up a continent and the thickness of its surface layers.

At every mile, Ned and Charlie used a portable gravimeter to give them additional estimates of the ice thickness. A gravimeter has a small weight suspended on a spring. The force of gravity pulls the weight down, and controls on the instrument measure the force required to bring the weight back to its original position. Since changes in the thickness of ice will affect this force, the variations in the force required, when studied along with seismic soundings, are another means of calculating the ice thickness.

These gravity observations also enabled Ned and Charlie to speculate on the nature of the rocks beneath the ice. When the nature of them changed, it, too, affected the readings.

While these two men were studying the thickness of the ice, Bill Long and Vernon Anderson were studying that part of it close to the surface.

As soon as the Sno-Cats rolled to a stop, Bill and Vernon began digging a 12-foot pit. The snow was hard and heavy. They had to throw it high up over the pit's edge and make sure it didn't fall back in. They worked furiously. Sometimes they became so hot while shoveling that they stripped off their parkas and their shirts. It was a curious sight to see two bare-chested men shoveling snow in the middle of the endless frozen expanse of the Antarctic!

Once the snow pit was dug, the two glaciologists could begin their research. At regular intervals down the pit well, they measured the temperature. Next they took samples of the snow. They collected these in tubes three inches in diameter and eight inches long. Since the density of a known volume can be figured out from its weight, they carefully weighed the samples. Thus they were able to compute the closeness with which the individual snow grains were packed together. Then they examined the wall of the pit closely to see if there were any differences in the various layers.

Measuring temperature in snow pit

The snow falling on the ice cap sometimes builds up in layers, each successive snowfall on top of the last. Bill and Vernon knew that the snow near the top of the pit was the most recent. The lower into the pit they looked, the farther back in time they would be peering. At the bottom of their pits they discovered snow which had fallen ten or fifteen years previously. They could tell the difference from the compactness of the layers and the thin sheets of ice between them.

After the snow pit had been explored, Bill drilled a still-deeper hole with a coring auger. This hollow drill can bring up a core of snow two feet long by three inches around. At a depth of 30 or more feet he measured temperature again. By plotting temperatures over the several-hundred-mile route of the traverse it was possible to draw a map showing what the climate of the remote parts of the ice cap is like. At thirty feet

Coring auger

down, the temperature represents the average yearly temperature at that location.

Jack Long also dug a snow pit. His pit wasn't square like his brother's. It was rectangular, with neatly carved ledges along the sides. After the pit was dug, Jack drove the Sno-Cats one by one over the pit. Here he greased them. The snow ledges were his workbench. At almost every stop he had to work on the Sno-Cats. After bounding along over the rough sastrugi the tracks had to be tightened, weak points in the frames welded. Jack was a skillful and imaginative mechanic. When he needed a small part he didn't have, he made it himself.

In these ways Charlie's traverse studied the ice cap in greater detail than men had ever been able to do before. They weren't rushing to a romantic objective such as the Pole. They were hunting for secrets that couldn't be obtained in a hurry. For instance, where was the

Greasing Sno-Cat

trench that Gould thought bisected the continent? How deep and wide was it?

After a day's work at a station they would spend a day driving, stopping for readings of the ice cap's altitude and for making additional gravity measurements. Then they would spend another whole day digging pits, shooting off seismic charges, and maintaining their vehicles. For three months the routine rarely changed. Only in bad weather would they be halted.

The most exciting experience Charlie Bentley had, occurred during the summer of his first long traverse. This was in 1957–58. He had reached the Sentinel Mountains. As he started back toward Byrd Station he noticed that the ice depths increased with each seismic test. One afternoon he could hardly believe his eyes as he looked at the records. His shot had measured more than 14,000 feet of ice. Since they were 5,000 feet above sea level this meant that the ice extended almost two miles *below* sea level to the rock floor.

Charlie had discovered the trench that Larry Gould suspected. It existed all right, though not where Larry had thought. It was a great ice-filled trough running

The Bentley traverse en route

from the Ross Sea through Byrd Land toward the Amundsen-Bellingshausen Sea area. Probably it separated the Palmer Peninsula and outer Marie Byrd Land from the rest of the continent. Locating it was the most important geographic discovery made in Antarctica in recent times.

While Bentley and his group were making their discoveries, other scientists from the United States, Great Britain, France, Australia and the Soviet Union were also examining the surface of the continent and what lay beneath it.

What new picture of Antarctica emerged from these IGY expeditions? Here is a bird's-eye view of what we know now. The eastern surface of the Antarctic rises gradually in a great dome between the South Pole and the Indian Ocean. We know that the highest point, at the center, is close to 13,000 feet. Because the snow at this elevation is very soft, we suspect the snowfall is light in this region and the winds much calmer than they are at the coast. From the high area the ice plateau slopes gently to the coast. The ice in this valley seems to be flowing.

The South Pole

This eastern part of the continent appears to be bordered on the sides that face the Ross Ice Shelf, Marie Byrd Land and the Weddell Sea by a more or less continuous range of mountains, whose rocks are alike. The winds are severe, except in the center. Along the Wilkes coast they have been known to blow as hard as 150 miles per hour. The temperatures are equally tough — as low as −120 degrees F. in the interior.

In West Antarctica, as in the east, more snow falls in the parts nearer sea level. The rest of West Antarctica, however, is completely different from the east. In Byrd Land many mountains mark the surface. Some are volcanic in origin. Others seem to have pushed up from the sea 75 million years ago. The temperatures are not so cold. The coldest recorded at Byrd Station is −78 degrees F.

Two great floating ice shelves, the Ross and the Filchner, extend far into the continent. The Ross Ice Shelf averages between 900 and 1,100 feet in thickness, of which only 120 to 200 feet stick up above sea level. A canyon in the ocean floor runs along the southern side of the shelf. A similar canyon has been found next to the Pensacola Mountains, on the east coast of the Filchner Ice Shelf.

The Sentinels look like a continuous mountain chain running from the Andes-like mountains of the Palmer Peninsula to the Queen Mauds, but we aren't yet certain that these mountains are connected. Charlie Bentley's channel appears to separate the Sentinels from the coast. We will know more when more ice thickness measurements are made.

The challenge of the sub-ice surface has caught hold

of Charlie Bentley, who returned to Antarctica in 1960. Bill Long went back to study fossils and coal in the Horlick Mountains in an effort to determine their age. His brother Jack went back to tend the Sno-Cats.

Vernon Anderson joined the U. S. Army's Cold Regions Research and Engineering Laboratory. Ned Ostenso went on with geological studies and analysis of IGY information.

Their interest is in the Antarctic surface and subsurface. Along with them have gone others intent on wresting secrets from its skies. What success has been theirs? For clues, we turn to Bucky Wilson in his Antarctic "observatory."

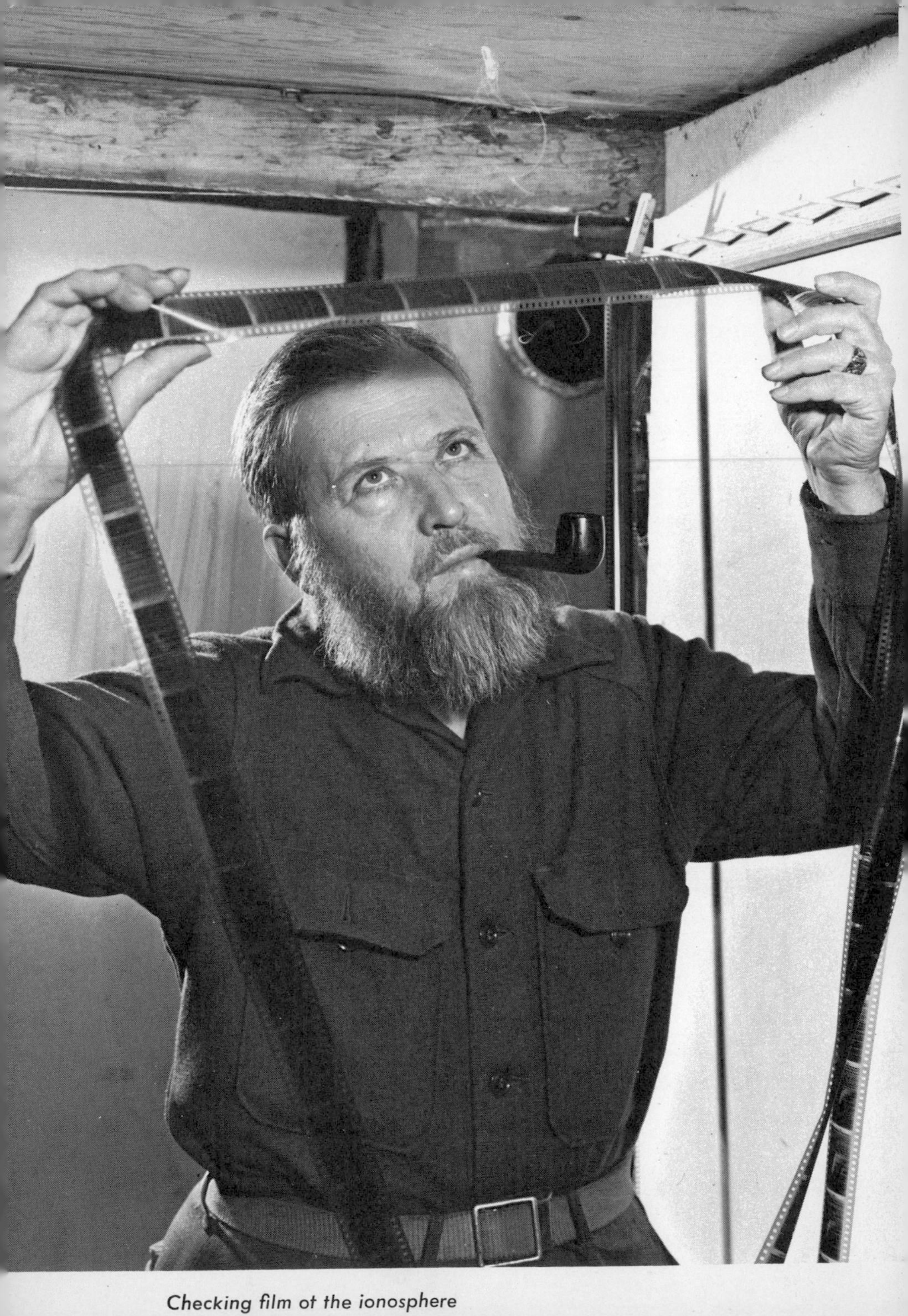

Checking film of the ionosphere

3. To the Edge of Space: Probing Antarctic Skies

EVERY NIGHT Bucky gets up and has breakfast. He sleeps during the day. It doesn't make any difference, for it's Antarctic winter and dark 24 hours a day. Only the silence around camp tells Bucky that it's nighttime.

Charles R. Wilson, which is Bucky's full name, came to the Antarctic at twenty-nine, after studying physics at the Case School of Applied Science in Cleveland, Ohio, and the University of Alaska. While in Alaska, he farmed on the side. There he got used to the heavy hat, gloves and parka he puts on now as he heads for the station's science building. Outside its back door is a covered, protected area. Inside this area, a ladder leads straight up 20 feet to a trap door. The trap door is the entrance to Bucky's tower laboratory.

The 8′x16′ lab is crowded. Four or five instruments are mounted in the roof. The shafts that support them don't leave much room for Bucky.

Sleepily, he clambers up onto a platform, unzips a cloth cover and sticks his head outside. All is black. The wind is blowing. Snow particles strike his face where the wool mask doesn't cover it. The air is very cold. Any sleepiness left, disappears.

Slowly Bucky's eyes become adapted to the dark. Above the blowing snow he sees a few stars. A light or two from the camp below are visible. Then Bucky notices a greenish patch in the sky to the east. His eyes are becoming more sensitive. Bucky sees the green light flicker and move. It's becoming brighter, and moving

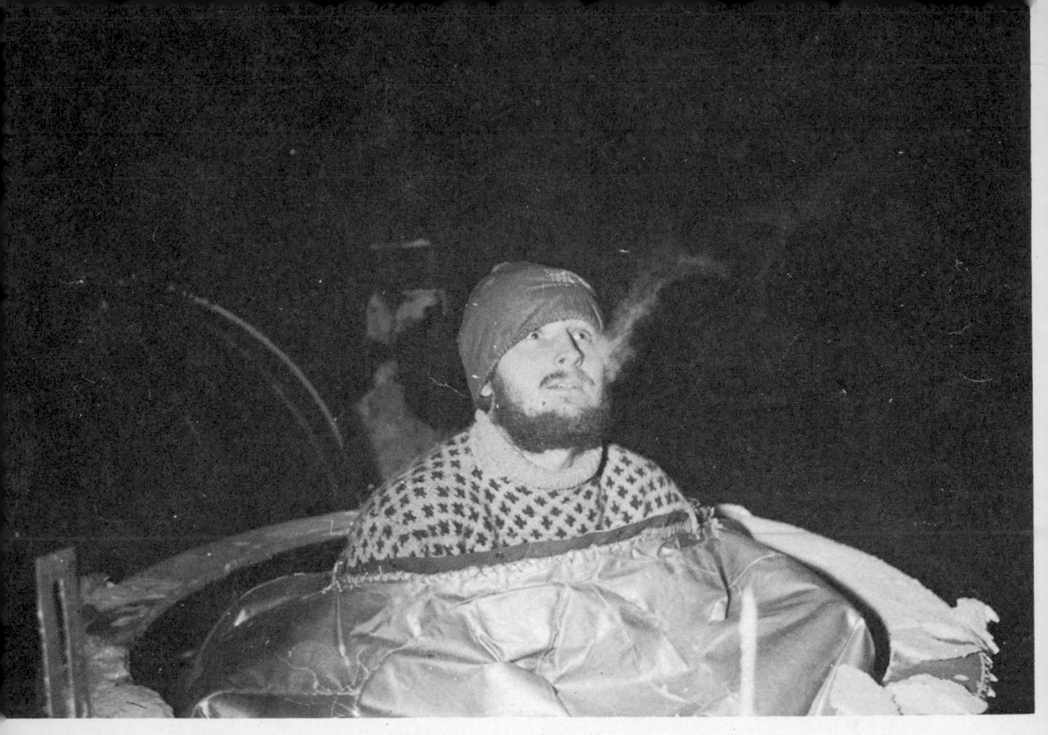

Bucky Wilson emerging from his tower

Bucky checks a laboratory instrument

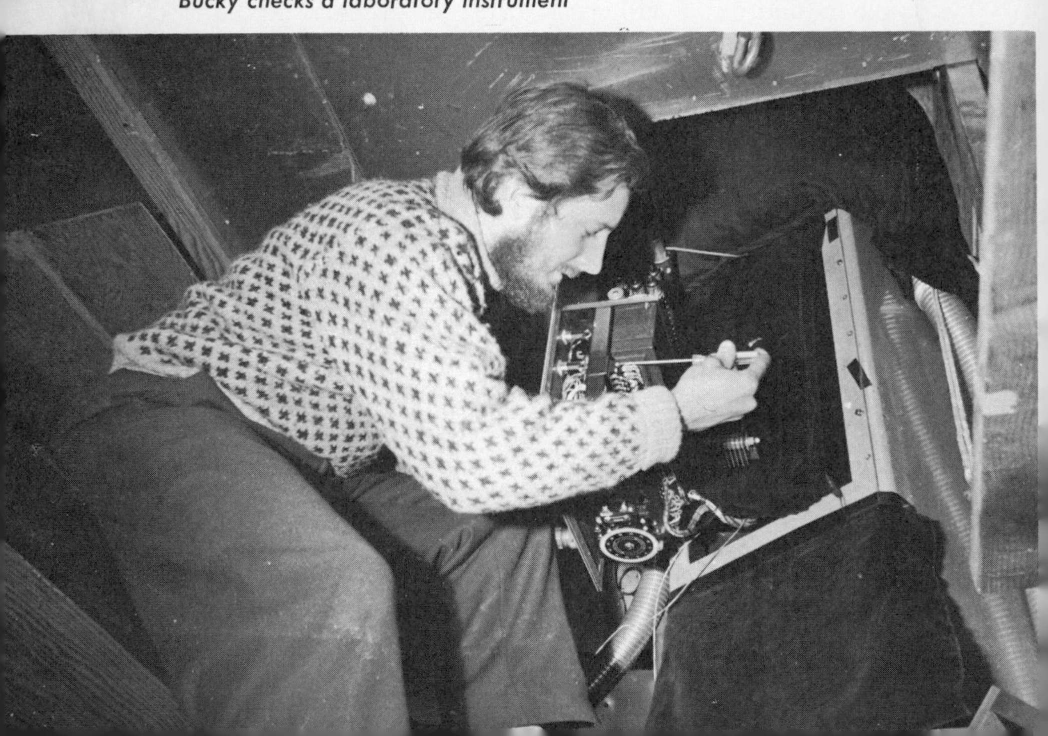

up the sky toward the zenith overhead. This is the aurora australis, the southern lights.

For the next ten or twelve hours Bucky will watch them grow brighter and larger and then disappear. His instruments will record their movement and brightness. He must make certain that these instruments will continue to operate while he sleeps the next day. In the black night sky, instruments alone won't do. He personally must watch and record what happens. There is no nighttime rest for the auroral observer until the summer sun brings 24-hour light.

Bucky has a heated plastic dome in the roof of his laboratory from which he can see the sky from horizon to zenith. During an auroral display he takes notes on what he sees. He measures where in the sky the aurora starts and in what directions it moves. He notes the shapes of the aurora. Sometimes it will be a shapeless mass. Sometimes it will hang in the sky like great curtains. Sometimes it will appear in tremendous shafts like the pillars of a cathedral. This shape is called a corona.

Bucky must also note the color. Most often the aurora appears as a pale whitish green, but sometimes it is purple or red. Sometimes these colors combine so that there is a red or purple border to a green aurora. And once every so often, in a great display, the whole sky will turn flame red, pulsating with great shafts shooting up into the sky. At these times it's hard for Bucky to take notes. He would rather just watch the display light up the entire station and the snow-covered continent as far as the eye can see. The aurora is never the same and is always fascinating.

From its features, many secrets of what is going on

in the atmosphere overhead are pieced together. The lower atmosphere which surrounds the earth is made up of molecules. They cluster most thickly near the earth, because gravity pulls them hardest there. Farther up, as gravity weakens, the molecules scatter.

Fifty to sixty miles above the earth, the molecule-scarce upper atmosphere, or ionosphere, begins. This is the realm of the ion, an electrically charged particle. Explosions of gases on the surface of the sun, and elsewhere in the space which lies beyond the atmosphere, produce radiation. As the radiation strikes the atmosphere of the earth, it changes the make-up of the ions. This change causes, among other things, the southern lights that Bucky is studying.

To assist him in his study, Bucky has a variety of instruments. Once every minute, or oftener if necessary, his camera takes a picture of the whole sky. Another instrument, his spectrograph, separates out the different wavelengths which make the light.

Ions of different substances give off different wavelengths when they are hit by radiation. To the naked eye these blend together into a single or several colors. But the spectrograph can separate out each color and record all of them on a film in graph form. From the heaviness and range of the marks on his film graph, Bucky can tell in what direction and at what speed the ion particles are moving.

He can also tell what substances are giving off light during a particular display: oxygen, hydrogen, sodium or some others. Then he uses his photometer. This measuring device shows him how much of a contribution each substance is making to the whole.

When it's cloudy or snowing, these photographic instruments are useless. Then Bucky uses radar to tell him whether an aurora display is occurring.

One scientist who is especially interested in Bucky's findings is twenty-one-year-old John Gniewek from Frankfort, New York, who graduated as a physics major from the University of Syracuse. John is a geomagnetician, a student of the earth's magnetism, its attraction for oppositely charged electrical particles such as ions. The earth acts like a very large magnet for these elements. Sometimes, however, there are changes in the magnetism the earth exerts. These are caused by bursts of radiation from the sun and are called magnetic storms. John's instruments have just recorded such a storm. Neither he nor anybody else in the station could feel or see it. But he thinks that Bucky may have seen the effects, the southern lights.

John's information about the storm comes from a magnetograph, an instrument which shows just how

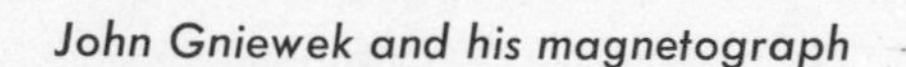

John Gniewek and his magnetograph

much the magnetism of the earth is changing. The instrument consists of small bar magnets with mirrors attached, and a circular drum covered with photographic paper and driven by a clock.

The magnets hang on quartz threads suspended from metal clamps. Light hitting the mirrors is reflected into the box which contains the drum. The drum is driven by the clock and revolves once every 24 hours. When the reflected light, entering the box through a slit, hits the piece of photographic paper on the drum, it leaves a small black line. When the earth's magnetism changes, it moves the magnets very slightly. Consequently, the spot of light reflected from the magnets' mirrors onto the photographic paper also moves. The movement lifts the small black line up on the paper. Later John can measure this movement and tell how much the earth's magnetism has changed.

Of course, the change in the black line may not always be caused by a magnetic storm. It may be that the ice beneath the station is moving or a tractor has come too near the building. These rumbles can produce the same effect. John has to do some complicated mathematics to make certain that the record has not been influenced by such happenings.

When he is dead sure of his observations, he will send them to other Antarctic magnetic observatories and to the United States. He does this at least weekly. This information is used in periodic world-wide reports on how the earth's magnetism is behaving.

The information is also important in radio communications. Within the earth's upper atmosphere, the magnetic field causes ions to arrange themselves in a kind of shield, which protects the earth from radiation and at the same time acts as a backstop for radio signals. Without this backstop, a radio announcer's voice would travel straight into outer space.

As it is, his voice, sent out by a transmitter, hits these shieldlike layers of ions anywhere from 75 to 200 miles above the earth and bounces back into the radio set. At the North and South Poles this shield is thicker than in other latitudes and more subject to effects of radiation and magnetic action. The Poles are, therefore, ideal for the study of the shield and its use in radio communication. Antarctica is preferable to the Arctic as a site for this study, because Antarctica has more land area from which to work. The Arctic is principally ocean.

An Antarctic student of the ionosphere is Jim Burnham. He was twenty-two years old when he first went to the Antarctic, with degrees in physics from Brown University, Rhode Island, and the University of Connecticut. Jim's ionospheric sounder sends its signals straight up into the atmosphere. But unlike a radio signal which is always transmitted at one frequency, or carrier of a sound wave, Jim can send his signals from low to high. Back to Jim's receiver from the ionospheric shield come only those signals pitched high enough to hit it, but not so high as to go right through it.

Each transmission and receipt of a signal is referred to as a *sweep*. The sounder records the results of every sweep and a camera photographs its scope. From these records, Jim notes daily changes in the ionosphere. He notes, for example, diurnal variation. Diurnal variation explains why more radio stations can be picked up, with clearer tones, at night than during the day.

The sun's radiation, in daylight hours, makes the ionosphere more dense and higher from the earth. Without the sun for long periods, as in the Antarctic winter, one would expect the ionosphere to become steadily thinner until it disappeared. Then radio communications would be impossible. But Jim's records prove that the diurnal variation continues to occur without the sun. He doesn't yet know why, nor does anyone.

Nevertheless, there are times when there is a radio blackout which may last from a few minutes to several days. To learn what causes it, Jim talks to John Gniewek and Bucky Wilson. The reason is soon clear. Bucky says that a brilliant aurora occurred at the time of the blackout. John shows from his records that just before

Radio blackout

the blackout a rapid change took place in the earth's magnetism, with increasingly disturbed conditions following it. From this evidence, the three of them know that the earth has been subjected to a sudden burst of radiation from the sun which has created a magnetic storm in the upper atmosphere.

It is through such teamwork, not only among the men in a single station, but among all the stations in the Antarctic, that this frozen frontier is being made to yield secrets useful to all the world. Today the reports Jim sends to the National Bureau of Standards in the United States help predict on what frequencies, and at what times, radio communication will be clearest in different parts of the world. Tomorrow this data may lead to the selection of new and more effective frequencies.

It also leads to knowledge that is important to astronauts. Charged particles in the ionosphere and radiation from the sun are hazards which spacemen must overcome. The Poles provide an especially clear window on space. Through their Antarctic observations, scientists like Bucky and John are helping man conquer this new element, too.

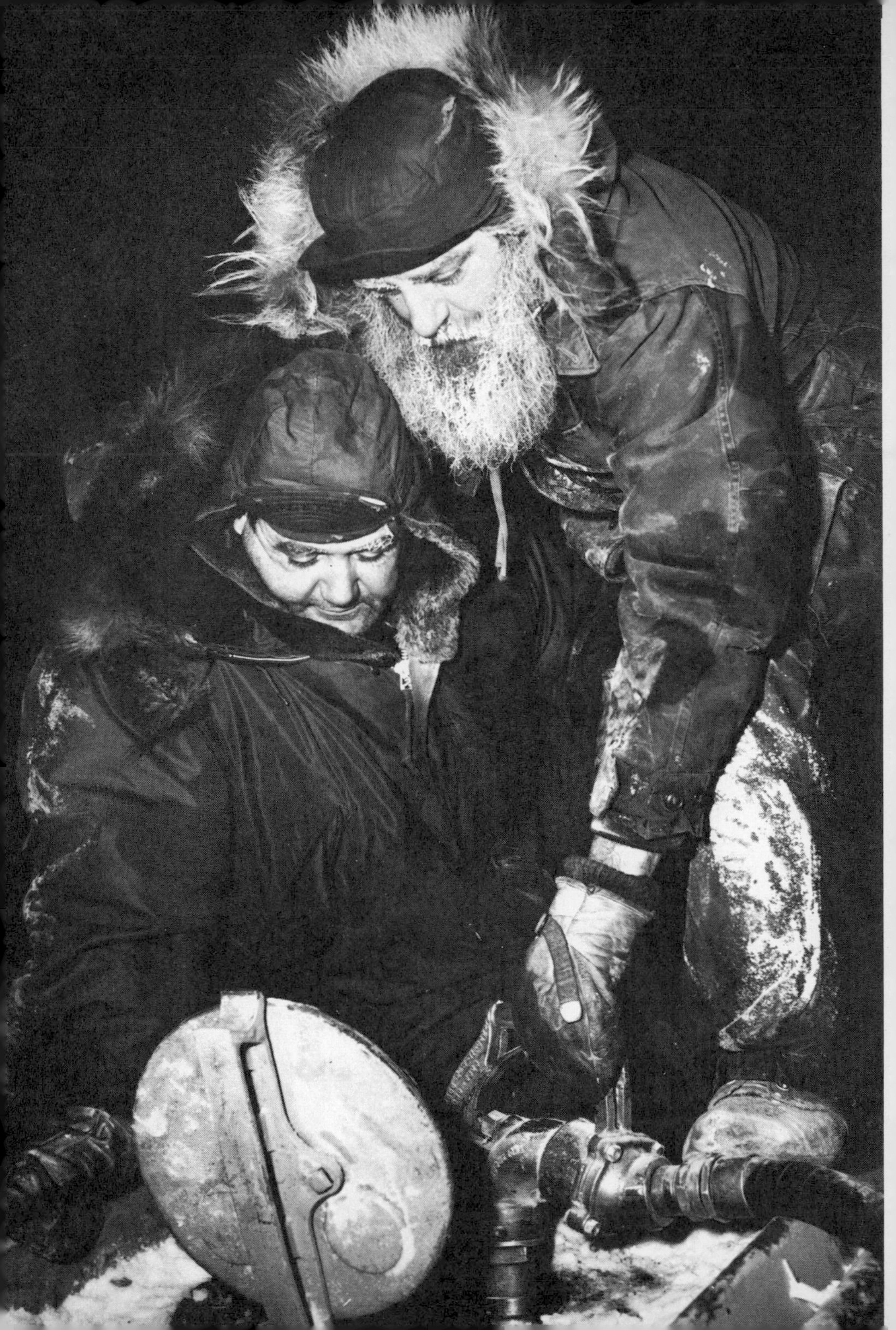

4. The Long Night of Winter

EVERYTHING IN ANTARCTICA is preparation. During the summer, men prepare for the next winter, and as they sit out the winter storms and wind and darkness, they ready equipment for the next summer.

"We work all day and we sleep all night and the night is six months long." This line from a popular Antarctic song is only partly true, for the winter is not a lazy time. Nor is it technically six months long. It just seems like it, because fall is really the beginning of winter. Fall and winter run from March through September, spring and summer from October through February. The seasons are just the opposite of those in the Northern Hemisphere.

In winter, the temperature averages 50 degrees below zero. There is no sun. The frozen continent is completely iced in from the outside world. There are no letters from home, no visitors — and it's a good idea not to fall seriously ill. Although there's a doctor at U. S. stations, only minor surgery, such as removal of an appendix, can be performed. Until the end of April, a man who needs more critical treatment can be flown out by ski-plane. But after April there's no possibility of help. Not even a ski-plane can get out.

In summer, there is no night. The sun shines 24 hours a day and the temperature may rise to 25–50 degrees above zero. The sea ice diminishes and there is much coming and going to and from and on the continent.

For those who are not on traverses, summer life back

at the station consists of shoveling snow, keeping open the runways for planes and the roads for tractors and sleds. Cargo is unloaded from ships, sledged to the station and stored for the coming winter. Some is reloaded for shipment by tractor and plane to field parties and stations deep in the ice-capped interior. Old buildings are repaired and new ones erected.

Often this work must be done in the midst of windblown snow and with constant interruption from storms. Sometimes everything that has been dug clear in a week of shoveling will be snowed over in a day. It is often so cold that metal can't be touched without gloves — a man's bare fingers will stick to it. If that happens, he may need a blowtorch to heat the metal so he can get his fingers off without leaving his skin behind.

At forty degrees below zero on a fine spring day, it takes two to start a Sno-Cat. A man and his buddy drag

a heavy gas heater from a shelter on a sled. They push ducts from the heater up into the engine and then fortify themselves with breakfast before the real struggle begins.

By the time they finish eating, the oil in the engine will have become warm. Now they can haul out and install the battery. Had they left it out overnight, it would have frozen, the same as the oil. Besides, the battery had to be taken inside to be recharged after travel in yesterday's cold. Even though it's been recharged, it takes the aid of a booster battery to get the engine going. The men lug that out and attach it. Gingerly, one of them tries the starter. If there's a little ice in the fuel line or the carburetor, they'll start over again with the heater and more batteries.

This morning they're in luck. The Sno-Cat starts. The driver leaves it running while digging out of yes-

Warming Sno-Cat engine with heater

terday's drifted snow the sled on which gear and food for the day will be piled. After tuning the radio and reporting on where they're going, in case of accident, the party is off.

In winter, men go outside as little as possible, but it's not possible to avoid outside work entirely. Every week or ten days, the big tanks that hold oil for the station's heaters and generators must be refilled. The oil drums are kept outside. Of course, they become buried deep under the snow.

Going after oil

Teams go after the oil. Everybody keeps a sharp eye out to prevent anyone from accidentally walking a few yards beyond the beam from the camp's searchlight. In blowing snow, this small distance can leave a man in total darkness, with no idea of which way to go. He can be utterly lost in a matter of seconds. Team members work in pairs that watch each other's faces. A man will suddenly see his buddy's nose go white with frostbite. Quickly the buddy is warned. He covers his nose with his hand to warm it, turns around so that the wind is at his back, and will soon be no worse for the narrow escape.

Snow mine

Water is another outdoor chore. Snow provides an infinite supply, but someone has to shovel it up and pour it down a chute into a snow melter. The snow must be clean because some of it will be used to drink. Every camp has a snow mine — an area located upwind from the camp so that it can't be polluted by smoke. Neither men nor vehicles are permitted in it, except to procure drinking-snow. Scooped up and carried to the station, the snow is dumped into an enormous tank partially filled with warm water. Since dry snow will evaporate on contact with hot metal, someone must always keep an eye on the snow melter to be sure of its water level.

Snow melter

Radio antenna repair

Occasionally damage to equipment will call for an outdoor task force. A high wind may blow away a section of antenna. Then there is nothing to do but pile on all the cold-weather clothing one has and go out to see what can be done. At best, it may be a minor repair job. At worst, it may mean climbing up a high pole in a howling gale, to install a new section by searchlight.

For the most part, however, winter work is inside. The buildings are constructed like iceboxes, but their purpose is to keep heat in, not out. They are made of standard panels, four feet wide by eight feet long and about four inches thick. The panels are filled with insulation to contain heat. They can be put together to make a building of any size, as long as it's a multiple of four by eight.

One of the most modern ways to set these buildings so that they won't be deformed or crushed by the winter's snow is to put them in a trench. Cut with a special plow, a Peter Snow Miller, the trench is wider at the bottom than the top. The top is narrower so that beams can be laid across it. These beams make up what is called a form. The Miller blows fine particles of snow over this form. The snow sets like cement or plaster, achieving great strength. Once it has set, the form below may be removed from the inside. Thereafter, all that's necessary is to shave the underside of the snow arch periodically so that it keeps a uniform thickness, even though more snow is piling on top of it from outside.

The future Antarctic camp, however, may well be built on stilts. Wind funneling under the buildings would help keep them free from drifts. Cargo elevators of the sort used in large aircraft would form part of the floor. They could be lowered on cables to pick up cargo. The structure on stilts would also have good visibility for scientific observations.

These observations must go on, whether summer or winter. In the winter, they may mean long hours at a desk, working over the summer's results and putting them in order. This job is known as *reduction of data.* Usually the data is coded into numbers arranged as a message. This message is then sent home via shortwave radio for immediate use. Information used in predicting weather and broadcasting conditions is sent in this form.

Complicated electronic equipment is used to record results. The equipment may need wintertime repairing or even complete rebuilding. Every day someone in the station will need some new equipment or material that is packed in a storeroom box or is buried in a cache outside. A station nearby may radio a request for a small part for an engine or a vital piece for an instrument. Not a day passes that someone doesn't have to help move a heavy box out of the storeroom into the light and crack it open with a crowbar. Then inventory lists must be changed to note the removal of the item before the box is moved back again.

The electrician at such a station is vital. Not only does equipment for scientific observations depend on electricity, but it would be a dreary life for the men without electric power. Of course, there are lanterns and flashlights and nonelectric heaters, in case of a power failure, but without electricity there would be no movies, no talking with the family at home over ham radio, no power tools for making repairs.

Power is provided by several diesel-electric generators. They must run all the time and their existence is a fire hazard. Therefore, a trained electrician must watch them all the time. Minor accidents with serious consequences can happen to the electric circuit at any hour. A rising temperature outdoors may make a tunnel start to drip as the snow above it melts a little. The drip may cause a short, burning out an important fixture or wire.

Another full-time job for several men is minding the radio, the station's only contact with the outside world from March to October. Radio is used to transmit data, order supplies for next year, make arrangements for men who will be leaving Antarctica in the summer, and talking with another station. Poor weather and magnetic troubles may make radio operation difficult. The patient operator may sit for hours with his headset on and his key in front of him as, word by word, he passes and receives his messages.

The mechanic, meanwhile, is busy in his machine shop. During summer, he is lucky if he can keep up with the daily small repairs required in the hard-used vehicles. Big repairs are winter jobs. The mechanic and his helpers may even have to haul in a big D-8 tractor from a snowdrift and completely rebuild it.

Repairing portable kitchen which is towed by Sno-Cat on traverse

Sleds, too, have to be repaired, sometimes rebuilt. Canned or dehydrated food must be packed in boxes, ready for next summer's traverses. Batteries, tents, sleeping bags, ropes — all must be ready to go when the sun rises again.

In the winter dark, each man has his household chores. Each takes his turn as *house mouse*. The house mouse sweeps the cubicle where he and one or two companions live, washes down the floors and empties the trash. Everybody washes his own clothes in the station washing machines.

Despite all these tasks, there is still time for play. At most Antarctic stations, the Saturday night double-feature movie and the Sunday afternoon matinee are popular. Even if you have seen the same Western six times, it loses none of its adventure the seventh time in Antarctica!

Tournaments are organized in such games as shuffle-board, bridge, pool or ping-pong. Sometimes the tournaments spread to interstation play carried on by radio. When an American station played chess with a Soviet station, everybody on both sides kibbitzed! Unfortunately, the arrival of summer and traverse time interrupted the long-drawn-out tournament before anybody won it.

An excuse for a good party can almost always be

found, but the traditional Antarctic party is midwinter's night, June 22. Most stations declare this date a holiday. Homemade drums, a few banjos and guitars may serve as an orchestra. There is generally someone who can sing or act, and it isn't long before everybody gets into the show.

The *Penguin Post* or the *Southern Times* or other such station newspapers occupy the winter leisure of both editors and readers. These journals present international news gleaned from shortwave, along with station gossip. They print results of station tournaments, also crossword puzzles, hot editorials and poetry. The editors take their weekly deadlines as seriously as though they were publishing a great daily in Washington, D. C.

Other men organize winter classes. Almost every explorer knows something he can teach someone else. Consequently, there are classes in such subjects as radio code, electronic repair, first aid, Russian or another foreign language, calculus and modern American history. Soon the students seek out reference books. There is a library in every Antarctic station. Most of these are augmented by volumes each man has beside his bed and the total provides more than can possibly be read in one winter by even the most avid bookworm.

When the shut-in explorer is tired of mental exercise, there's always the gym. When winter comes a gym will appear at most stations, with improvised mat and equipment. Mix a physical workout with a tournament or two, a class in Russian, an article for a newspaper, a chapter about early Antarctic explorers, three good meals and a movie — and a man has a hard time getting his required work done on an Antarctic winter's day!

But with the first rays of the new sun, life changes sharply. It is time to be up and out and discovering. The summer months ahead are few and short. The continent is big and still unknown!

The flag goes up at McMurdo Base when the sun comes out again.

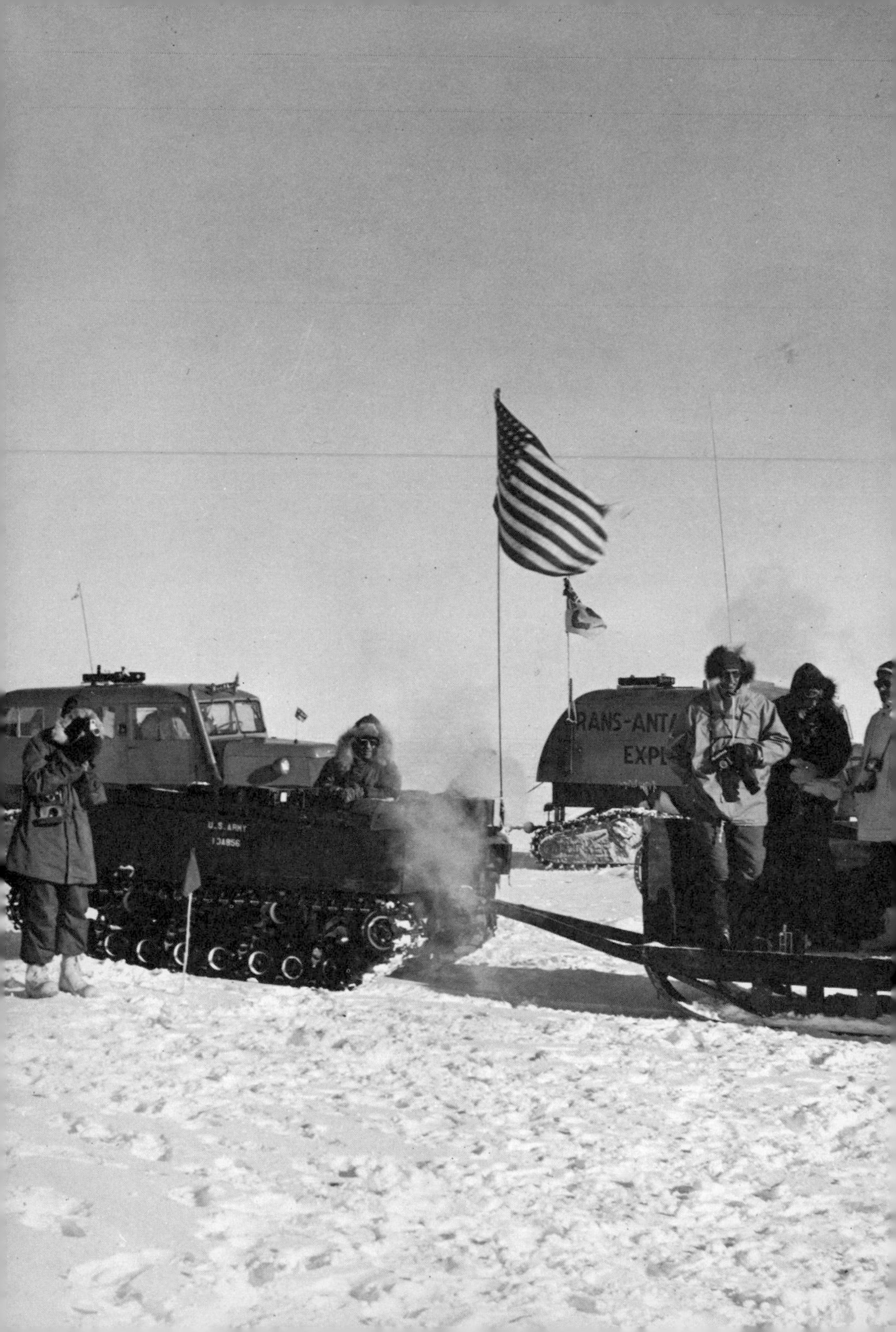
U.S. ARMY
RANS-ANTA
EXPL

5. By Sky Train and Tractor Train: Summer Traverse

THE SCIENTIFIC PARTY departing from a station is a colorful sight. Two or three Sno-Cats, lined up side by side, belch great white clouds of exhaust vapor into the crisp air. Sleds with platforms about 6 by 12 feet in size are piled high with gear. The sleds carry fuel drums, cases of food, explosives for seismological exploration, bamboo poles and flags, spare parts for vehicles, and drills with long pipelike extensions for making shot holes in the ice cap. On top of these are skis and poles, dufflebags of spare clothing and extra ropes. Pairs of giant rubber tires are pulled behind the sleds of one or two of the Sno-Cats. Each of these *rollitankers* contains 500 gallons of gasoline. They are much easier to pull than sleds. Fuel is pumped directly from the tires into the Sno-Cats.

The lead cat flies the national flag. Usually several pennants wave from the other cats and sleds. The pennants are from the scientists' home states, their college clubs and other places where they have been attached. After a big last-minute bustle, much as when starting on a long family vacation, the party is ready to go. The Sno-Cats start with a great jerk. The occupants wave good-by to their companions at the station. Soon the station is a speck on the horizon behind the Sno-Cats as they bounce along over the sastrugi.

Driving across the ice cap is something like sailing across the ocean. There are few landmarks. The trail party must depend on the sun to chart its direction. One of the party establishes position by it at each stop and sets a course that corrects errors made in driving across the irregular wind-blown surface.

Radio contact must be maintained with the station. Long before the traverse leaves, one of its members starts practicing radio code. He doesn't become as skillful as a regular radio operator, but he can transmit the party's latitude and longitude, the plans for the next day, and request assistance if it's needed. He can repair the equipment when it breaks down.

Some of the caravans crossing the ice cap are supply parties. Their job is to bring food, fuel and building materials to inland stations far from the coast. They travel in tractor trains, with four to eight thirty-ton Caterpillar tractors to each train. Their extra-wide tracks keep them from sinking into the snow. Each tractor pulls two monstrous sleds, loaded with 20 tons of supplies apiece.

Tractor train

With all this weight, the tractors can't go very fast, only about three to four miles an hour, but they are a marvelous sight as they ply back and forth over Antarctic trails. If the wind is right, you can hear their roar from a great distance before you can actually see the black diesel exhaust of their stacks.

One of the tractors generally pulls one or two houses. The drivers call the houses their *wanigans*. Wanigans are where they take turns sleeping as, operating around the clock, the train pushes on over the ice cap. Sometimes there is a separate wanigan for cooking.

The snow-filled crevasses are especially treacherous hazards for these tractor trains. Before a train sets out, an advance party scouts the trail. The scouting party is equipped with dynamite, a Caterpillar tractor with a 16-foot-wide dozer blade on it and a Sno-Cat or other light vehicle with a crevasse detector attached.

The crevasse detector is made up of four dishpan-

Crevasse detector

shaped electrodes at the end of wooden booms ten feet long. From the air it looks like a big spider. Two electrodes transmit a signal that travels down through the snow. The signal is picked up by the other two electrodes. If the signal path through the snow becomes altered, as it does when the electrodes are over the dead air space of a snow-bridged crevasse, the driver of the detector vehicle gets a flashing light on his control panel. He slows to a stop with his heart in his mouth. He wonders whether he can stop before the front of his vehicle goes into the crevasse!

If the tractor trail must cross the crevasse, one of the party members goes down into it. He climbs down on a flexible cable ladder, or slides down on a rope. Once inside, he investigates the size of the crevasse and especially the thickness of the snow bridge above him.

The interior of a crevasse is awesome and beautiful. Near the surface where sunlight penetrates, the walls are a light blue. Sometimes the banding of annual snow accumulation shows. At a greater depth the crevasse has a deep blue appearance. In the shadowy bottom, at about 100 or 120 feet, it is purple. Pure white mounds of snow mark places where sections of the bridge have fallen in the past. On walls where tremendous strains have worked the ice, grotesque ice gargoyles show pale green in the subdued light.

After the crevasse is inspected, dynamite charges are set to blow off the snow bridge across the top. In the spectacular explosion, plumes of snow shoot high into the air. Next, the tractor, with its wide blade, pushes the snow over the brink until the crevasse is full. It is then safe to drive over.

Inside crevasse

Dynamite charge

Tractor pushing snow

The route finally inspected by the advance scouts is marked with flags on bamboo poles set into the snow. Then the tractor trains can lumber and rumble on to the inland outposts.

Other field parties use aircraft equipped with skis. The aircraft with skis has revolutionized techniques of exploring the Antarctic. The explorer can fly over it and see great areas in the course of a few hours. He can map many parts of the continent in a single summer.

Ski-plane fliers can search out routes for tractor trains, deliver scientists and supplies even to the South Pole itself.

The Douglas Skytrain, or two-engined DC-3, is the most famous plane in Antarctic aviation. It was the first to land at the South Pole. Equipped with two large skis on its main wheels and a smaller ski under the tail, this rugged plane can land and take off practically anywhere on the ice cap. For long flights it is equipped with an extra fuel tank in the cabin. When sastrugi are rough or the altitude high, the DC-3 gets a special boost in take-off from jet bottles fired by the pilot. These JATOs (*J*et *A*ssisted *T*ake *O*ff) are fastened to the fuselage not far behind the main wing. When the JATOs are fired the passengers inside hear a loud roar as the plane leaps into the air.

Other well-known planes in the Antarctic are the Navy's Lockheed Neptune P2V and Lockheed C-130, or Hercules. Besides regular skis, the Neptune has a nose ski which is raised up against the fuselage when the plane is in flight. From its nose there is a marvelous, unobstructed view through a bubble-shaped plexiglass window. The plane is used for mapping and scouting.

JATO

P2V Neptune

The Hercules combines the characteristics of a large cargo plane with the maneuverability of a small passenger plane. Using powerful turboprop propellers, it can take off with a ten-ton load from a runway only 1,500 feet long. Its mammoth skis form part of the fuselage when not extended for landings and takeoffs. The two main skies weigh a total of five tons.

In contrast with these air giants are helicopters. HUL and HUS are the models used in American operations. HUL, the smaller of the two, is used especially by ships. It nestles on the deck between flights. Good visibility from the cockpit makes it valuable in ice recon-

Hercules

naissance for convoys. The HUS has a long range and is an excellent rescue plane. It once flew 200 miles from any landmarks to rescue an injured geologist isolated on a high polar plateau.

The helicopter can land and pick up scientists where no other plane can venture. One scientist was plunged into the frigid water of Kainan Bay off Little America. It was getting toward winter and all the ships had returned north. He climbed up onto an ice flow figuring that this was the end. But rescue came — via helicopter.

Geologists and glaciologists find the helicopter almost

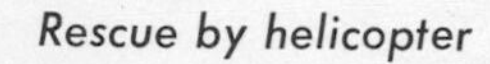

Rescue by helicopter

HUL over Weddell Sea

indispensable. With it, they have explored ice-free valleys near McMurdo Station. They have penetrated the heart of a heavily folded and crevassed area on the Ross Ice Shelf. There, the ice is pushed up into peaks and bumps not unlike the way the earth's surface bulges into mountains.

Another valuable small plane is the single-winged, single-engined DeHaviland Otter. Equipped with skis, the Otter can take off or land in 600 to 800 feet when unloaded. With a 7,600-pound load, it can take off or land in 1,200 feet.

In the Otter, biologists can repeat Cherry-Garrard's month-long trip from Cape Evans to Cape Crozier in half an hour! They can safely bring back to their laboratory at McMurdo samples of lichens, penguins and the plankton found in small lakes made by melting snow.

In 1959, the Otter was used for one of the strangest flying operations ever undertaken in the Antarctic. Scientists from the Bishop Museum in Honolulu began a study of the airborne scattering of insects in the South Pacific. Nets were mounted on a boomlike frame extending from the Otter's fuselage. Flying at 10 or 20 feet above the ice and land surface, the Otter looked like a weird-winged bird with pastel-colored nets fastened to its sides. It returned with nets as empty as when it left — proving that the insects sought weren't around this part of Antarctica. Antarctic insects have been discovered, however, by a high-speed plane with a trap attached.

Whatever the type of plane, weather prediction is important to its pilot. The network of weather stations

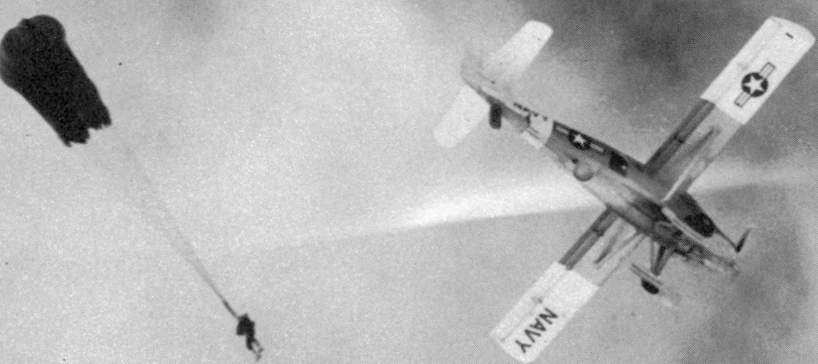
NAVY

in the Antarctic is manned by meteorologists from many nations, often working together in the same stations.

One of these meteorologists was Paul Dimitrevich Astapenko, an exchange scientist from the Soviet Union. He was assigned to a United States station in Little America. To follow his work, we'll have to track a balloon.

Mapping weather

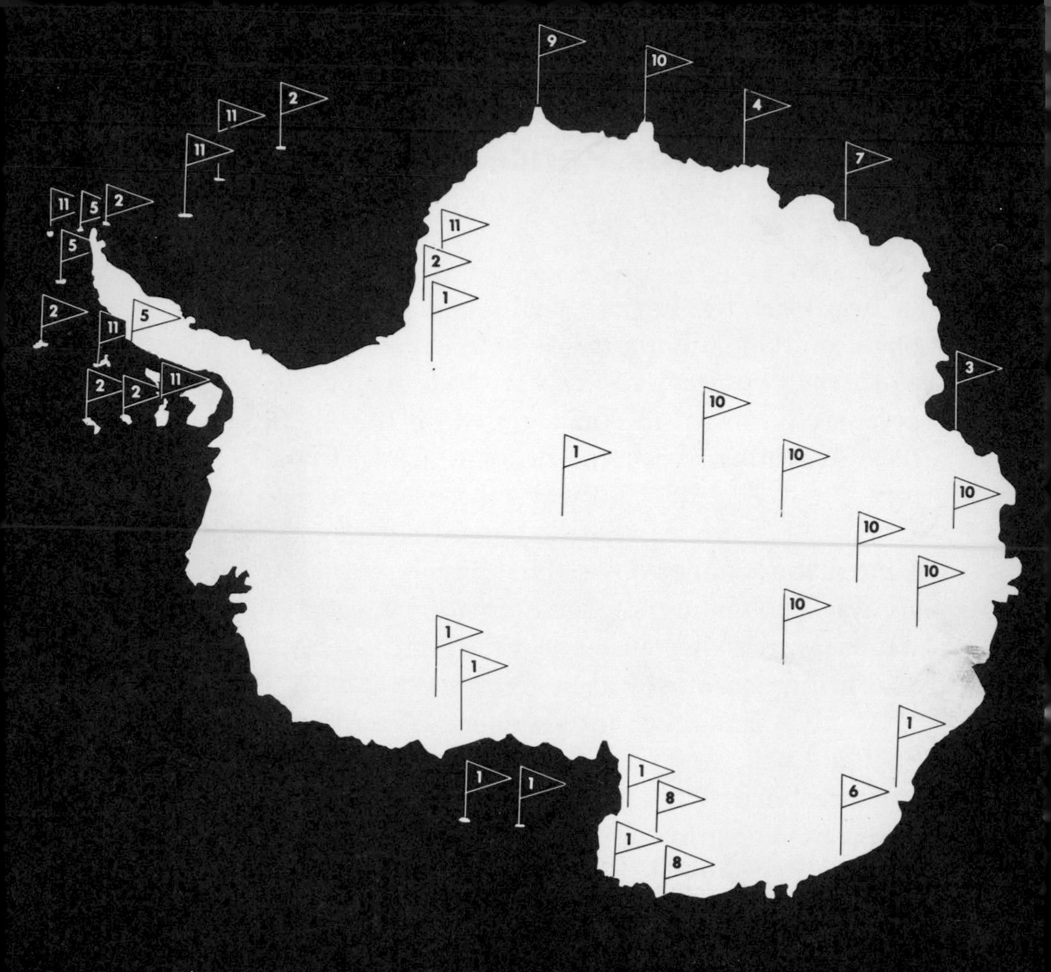

1 United States
2 Argentina
3 Australia
4 Belgium
5 Chile
6 France
7 Japan
8 New Zealand
9 Republic of South Africa
10 USSR
11 United Kingdom

Antarctic stations

6. Pattern for Peace and Progress

IT WAS 1958, the International Geophysical Year. One phase of IGY was the third Polar Year. In 1882 and 1932, the two previous years set aside for international polar study, men had concentrated on the Arctic. But now Argentina, Australia, Belgium, Chile, France, Japan, New Zealand, Norway, the Soviet Union, the Union* of South Africa, the United Kingdom and the United States undertook to establish 66 stations in Antarctica. The findings of the international teams in these stations were to become part of the body of world-wide information accumulated in celebration of IGY.

At the Antarctic International Weather Center, Station Little America, Paul Dimitrevich Astapenko, from the Soviet Ukraine, was working with four Americans, an Argentine, an Australian and a Frenchman. They were making daily weather maps for the Antarctic and forecasts which could be used by all the nations working together in the area.

Radio messages from all the Antarctic told Paul and his companions about the speed and direction of the wind in different parts. The messages relayed the degrees of temperature and humidity on the ground and at various levels up to heights between 60,000 and 100,000 feet.

Measurements at such heights are taken by a balloon sent aloft twice a day. The balloon is filled with hydrogen and a little box of instruments is attached to it. Through a radio transmitter, the instrument's record-

* Now Republic

Antarctic weather balloon

ings are sent back to earth. The operation is called a *radiosonde*. When radar is used to track the balloon, the observation becomes a *rawinsonde*. First it was necessary for one man to fill the balloon with hydrogen made in a large gas generator. Then, as he released the balloon from the inside of the generator shack, another man on the shack roof caught hold of the balloon's instrument box as it emerged through a trap door. He had to make sure it wasn't damaged by hitting anything. When the balloon was free, the man on the roof watched it go. At nighttime, he could sight it by a small light attached to it. Over station intercom, he called out the position of the balloon to a radar operator, who then located it on his set.

Once located, a balloon is automatically tracked by the radar. From balloons released all over the Antarctic, observers take down the data, radio it back and send it

Radar

on to Weather Central. By agreement, observers at all weather stations make their observations at the same times every day.

Back at Weather Central, Paul Astapenko put this sort of data onto maps and graphs. He then compared these for every recorded level of atmosphere and geographical location. First he compared the maps for a certain hour. Then he compared them for several days. From the long comparison, he was able to trace the consistent movement of mass air circulation in the Antarctic and surrounding areas. On this basis, he predicted what the weather would be 12 or 24 hours ahead for any given section of the continent. The weather message went out to all Antarctic stations, telling them what to expect. Six to 12 hours later, the process started all over again.

These meteorological facts are essential to Antarctic

Paul Dimitrevich Astapenko

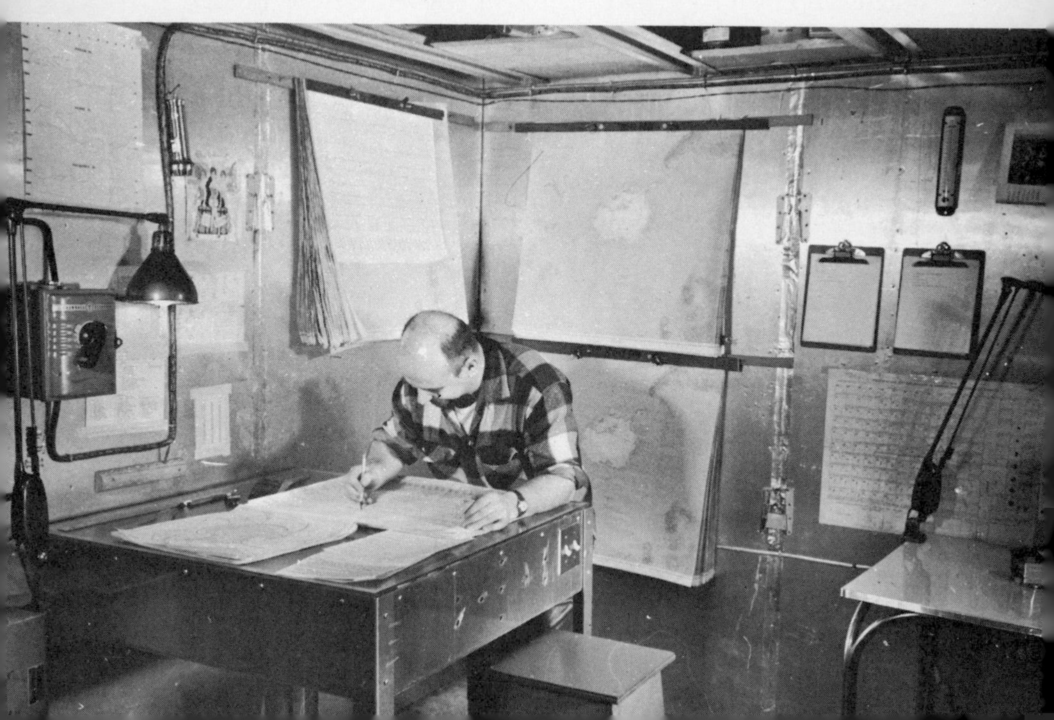

aviators. The findings also have a long-range usefulness to other parts of the world. It has long been known that weather patterns in New Zealand, Australia, South America and elsewhere in the Southern Hemisphere are influenced by what is happening in the Antarctic, but we have never known quite how. Now, from the growing picture of Antarctic air circulation, it's possible to find out.

The discoveries of Antarctic meteorologists are also useful to oceanographers and glaciologists. Antarctic winds affect waves and currents. They erode snow. The glaciologist trying to decide whether the ice cap is growing or shrinking in different parts of the continent needs to know in what areas snow will add to the cap, and in what areas winds will erode the snow. The meteorologist can answer his questions.

Cooperation between workers in many branches of science has turned the Antarctic into a great international laboratory. Their efforts in the Antarctic phase of the IGY were crowned with a great reward in October 1959. In that month, representatives of all the nations which had made IGY a success gathered in Washington, D. C. They were there at the invitation of the U. S. Government, to attend a conference on Antarctica. The result of the conference was the signing of the Antarctic Treaty on December 1, 1959, finally ratified on June 23, 1961.

The treaty sets the Antarctic aside for peaceful purposes only. It cannot be used by any nation as a base for military activities. It cannot be used as an atomic testing ground. Radioactive materials cannot be buried in its snows or dumped into its surrounding seas. For the time

Soviets at South Pole

being, there can be no borders, no boundaries, no fences, no territories to squabble over.

The treaty doesn't ask nations to give up claims which they had made before the treaty was proposed. It does, however, declare that these old claims are to be put on the shelf for a while and that no new ones will be made.

The treaty makes certain that the Antarctic will stay open to scientists of all cooperating nations. It urges them to exchange information. It fosters exchange of personnel and says that all countries are free to inspect each other's activities. It guarantees open skies. The planes of any of the 12 signers may fly over any part of the continent at any time and land at any station.

The importance of this treaty goes far beyond the icy edges of Antarctica. It may become a model for treaties governing other areas of the universe: for the oceans that cover more than 70 per cent of our world, and for the worlds that lie beyond in outer space. As in the Antarctic, exploration of these frontiers may be protected from national greed and international warmongering.

On the frozen continent itself, the treaty will speed up answers to the many questions still challenging polar scientists. Was the Antarctic once connected by a land bridge to one or more of its neighboring continents? If the answer is yes, then why did it break away to assume its solitary position at the southernmost end of the earth? What forces ruptured it?

In the high upper atmosphere above, why does the aurora australis occur simultaneously with a sudden disturbance in the earth's magnetic field? What is the aurora's relationship to rapid change in the ionosphere? What single principle may control all three events?

How does a penguin find his way back to the same rookery every year? Once there, the bird picks a mate, incubates the yearly egg and raises a chick in time for it to swim to sea with its parents at the end of the season. What tells the penguin the way home?

Why after why piles high as the snowdrifts for the men exploring the Antarctic today. Fortunately, not only the freedom provided by the Antarctic Treaty, but also new tools for exploration are at scientists' service in the search for the answers.

Rockets and polar-orbiting satellites will allow the physicist to chart the way in which earth's magnetism warps and bends the belts of radiation that surround it. Rockets will radio back information on the aurora and the ionosphere. Instruments at stations on the ground will continue to record the effects of these forces as seen from the surface of the earth, but no longer will the scientist have to guess what's happening up there from what he sees down here. He will be able to grasp the whole picture at once.

Rockets and satellites will also aid the Antarctic weatherman. Cameras in satellites circling the earth in paths over the Pole will photograph clouds, storm formations and ice pack conditions.

Automation — machines to do work that once required men — is on its way to the Antarctic. Automatic recording stations to be dropped from the air by parachute are being tested. They may broadcast weather data and other information several times a day for an entire year without being tended by men. A short summer trip for repairs would ready the automatic stations for another year of work.

Parachuting equipment

For manned stations, prefabs are on the way. These stations, small but complete in every detail needed for comfort and work, can be transported by aircraft and set up in a few hours. When the men have finished their work, the stations can be retrieved by plane and moved to a new site. Such stations can be built so that the only thing to be done is to unload them and plug them into their generators. Even the beds will be made before the prefabs are landed! Compact field laboratories can be built and transported in the same day.

Modern research ships, strengthened to withstand ice pressure, will give more access to the rich and unknown seas surrounding the Antarctic. Such ships will be equipped to observe the ocean floor, its currents, temperatures, the chemistry of its waters. They will be floating laboratories for the study of marine life. They will serve as platforms from which to make observations about the interior of the earth below the sea and the atmosphere above it. In fact, ships can do much the same kind of work in the Antarctic waters as the Sno-Cats do on ice. Gravity studies and underwater seismic explosions can determine how deep the sedimentary layer at the ocean bottom is and what the layers of it are like. Coring augers can bring up conesful of it. This ocean-bottom ooze is both a breeding place and burial ground for some of the most important sea organisms. It contains a record of geological time

With steam-shovel jaws, with nets and trawls and drags, sea life at all levels can be collected. From water samples, we can learn much about the circulation of currents and sources of minerals.

Marine research, Ross Sea

For the study of the southern atmosphere, a ship is a great convenience. Building stations on the continent itself and then moving them to study a new location every year is terribly expensive. A ship can relocate with no trouble at all. It can cover a far larger area than any land-based station. From its decks, meteorological balloons and rockets loaded with scientific instruments can be launched, anywhere, any time.

These are some of the new tools the modern scientific explorer in Antarctica will possess. With them he may be able to overcome radio blackouts as he discovers what controls the behavior of the upper atmosphere. He may even be able to discover entirely new means of sending messages through the atmosphere. He may be able to make the difference between success and failure for the New Zealand sheep rancher or the Australian wheat farmer by predicting the weather. He may discover how to extract more minerals from the sea and how to use its marine life to feed the hungry peoples of the world.

We already know that plankton, with which Antarctic seas abound, has nourishment for men and animals. We are beginning to find evidence that it may also contain antibiotics which can protect us from disease.

There are many Antarctic secrets yet to be defrosted. Were Australia, South Africa and India once connected to Antarctica? Did the sediments folded into the mountains of its western half come from some other now-detached continent? Is it even proper to speak of "the western half"? Can we talk of halves of one continent, or must we talk of two continents? Just how old is the ice on both? When were the ferns and trees frozen to

The mysterious continent

death? How come there are today 14,000 feet of ice only 800 miles from the mountains where we have discovered these plants once grew?

Some of these secrets affect the Antarctic only; others affect the world. Some may reach as far as the moon. From parts of the experience of living and working in Antarctica, of setting up or moving a research station, a young explorer may learn some errors to avoid in building a station on the moon.

There are parts of Antarctica as big as the states of Texas or Alaska where no studies at all have been made as yet. Now is the time. We have the freedom of inquiry guaranteed by the treaty. We have the tools provided by modern technology, tools of which young Captain Palmer, Lieutenant William Walker and Aspley Cherry-Garrard never dreamed. We have springboards into the unknown built by the young men of IGY.

Perhaps you may sledge or sail in their wake, for tomorrow, as in the past, the courage and curiosity of youth can play a great part in making this last unexplored frontier on earth yield its benefits to all the world.

Index

3
QUE SERÁ SERÁ

About the Author

ANN-MARIE MACDONALD is a Toronto-based writer and actor. Her play, *Goodnight Desdemona, Good Morning Juliet* won the Governor General's award for Drama, the Chalmers Award for Outstanding Play and the Canadian Authors' Association Award for Drama. She also appeared in the feature films *I've Heard the Mermaids Singing* and *Where the Spirit Lives*. This is her first novel.